Date Due

JOHN ADAMS

INDEPENDENCE FOREVER

by

Sybil Norton and John Cournos

Illustrated by Jacob Landau

HENRY HOLT and COMPANY • NEW YORK

JB
A

1-23-56

FIRST EDITION

Library of Congress Catalog Card Number: 54-5740

Printed in the United States of America.

For

Mary Richardson Satterthwaite

lineal descendant of several persons mentioned in
this book and heir to the traditions of independence and freedom sown nearly
two hundred years ago from
Maine to the Carolinas.

CONTENTS

CHAPTER ONE

BOYHOOD IN BRAINTREE

A LITTLE OLD LADY, SOLID AND PRIM, WITH AN expression severe yet kindly, stood one May morning at the door of a frame house. She was watching a group of young children, none older than ten, file out one by one into her spacious back yard and gather under a big apple tree.

There was a certain pride in her brown eyes as she observed the youngsters. All of them, whether tall or small, were sturdy, as became the offspring of hardworking farmers, themselves sons and grandsons of New England pioneers. She had her eyes on one boy in particular, the last to leave the house.

This boy was small, but chubby and especially sturdy. As she followed him to join the children under the tree, she thought what a fine youngster he was. One day he will come to something, she told herself.

1

She had a singular fondness for this little John Adams. The Adamses were her neighbors in the tiny town of Braintree, ten miles south of Boston, Massachusetts.

Little John, conscious of Dame Belcher's observation, suddenly turned to her—it was for this that he had lingered behind—and asked almost pleadingly:

"Mrs. Belcher, may we have a Scotch song today?"

"Surely, John. Provided you do a large share of the singing."

Mrs. Belcher smiled at her own little joke, for she well knew that John had a strong voice which sounded above the other voices, and that there was nothing he liked better than to make use of it in song.

There was no nonsense about Dame Belcher. Suiting her action to her words, she promptly addressed the circle of children:

"We are going to have a Scotch song. Which will you have?" Her face was turned to John at the back of the throng.

Unhesitatingly he called out: " 'Bonie James Campbell'!"

"Yes, let's have that!" a second voice echoed. It was the voice of his eight-year-old friend John Hancock, son of Reverend Hancock, minister of the Congregational meetinghouse.

In unison, the young voices struck up:

> " 'O it's up in the Highlands,
>   and along the sweet Tay,
>   Did bonie James Campbell
>   ride monie a day.

" 'Sadled and bridled,
        and bonie rode he;
  Hame came horse, hame came sadle,
        but neer hame came he.' "

"And now," said Dame Belcher, turning to John, "since you are feeling so energetic today, what about dancing a hornpipe?"

"Yes, yes, a hornpipe!" cried several voices.

Without waiting for a reply, four of the boys started imitating the hornpipe—the musical instrument so popular with sailors. The rest of the boys clapped their hands in time to the quick tune.

Urged on by the others and caught in the mood of the moment, young John, who loved dancing as he loved singing, sprang into the ring.

He raised and lowered and crossed and recrossed his short legs and plump arms, while his friends cheered and clapped.

"Well done, John! Well done!" came the spontaneous cries, as he abruptly stopped and sat down.

Three minutes later, Dame Belcher, who had disappeared into the house, reappeared with a large crock, from which she handed out cookies. She offered John a double portion, "as a reward for the energetic effort," as she put it.

These brief, after-school outings were customary with Dame Belcher. She began the lessons with the singing of a psalm, then put the boys through a rigorous morning of reading, writing, and arithmetic. In arithmetic, especially, she applied the use of figures to everyday life.

Young Adams liked her hard common sense and precision. He felt that under her instruction he was learning things. He liked going to her school.

On this particular morning—it was not the first time —she asked him to wait until the other children had gone.

"I have some grain," she said, "which I want ground into flour. I want you to help me take my grain to the mill. My husband—and a good farmer he was—used to do it when he was alive."

Dame Belcher and John Adams walked out of the front door. Between the door and the road stood an immense oak tree, visible for a long distance because it topped Penn Hill. Only from this point in all Braintree was the sea visible.

They carried the grain in pails. After the miller had ground the grain, they carried the pails filled with white flour back to the house.

"Here are three pennies for your trouble, John," she rewarded him, adding, "Save it up, Johnny, with the other pennies I've given you and any other pennies yet to come. When you have enough saved up, buy land with it. Nothing like land to make a worthy man."

Usually sparing of her words, on this day she surprised him by continuing: "Just look, Johnny!" She took a coin out of her purse and sent it rolling down the long kitchen table. "That's what the foolish man does with his money! He lets it roll away. The wise man does this." And, extracting several coins from her purse and laying one down flat, she slowly added coin after coin on top of it until the whole resembled a column.

"He piles it up," she went on, "then buys land—

acres and acres of it maybe! It doesn't mean you have to be a miser to do that, but merely sensible. All right, Johnny, enough for one day. I expect to see you in school tomorrow."

On reaching home, John, as always, was full of the morning's happenings. It was Dame Belcher this and Dame Belcher that! John was a talkative boy. His parents, especially his mother, always listened with interest, if sometimes with impatience. But as the afternoon wore on there were tasks and chores to be done.

"John," said his mother, a woman whose hands were never idle, "whittle me two or three pegs for the door to hang my aprons on."

John promptly went to work, and in no time he had the pegs ready. He was quick and skillful with the knife.

"John," said his mother after that, "now run out and fetch a few logs for the kitchen hearth." She herself was working over the cooking pots.

Presently John returned, his short arms filled with half a dozen logs which he laid down by the hearth.

"John," his mother called again, "now take this pail of slops and feed it to the pigs."

Before long John returned with the empty pail.

"Still one more thing, John," said his mother. "I see no one has brought in the cows. Bring them in and stanchion them. Your father is late. He'll likely be along in time to help you with the milking."

Much later John returned by himself, with one pail of rich milk for his mother's use. His father and younger brothers were just coming in from the fields. Peter Boylston was only six, and Elihu was a fat three-year-old.

After thoroughly washing at the kitchen pail, they took their places at the long table which stood in the middle of the spacious kitchen. Little Elihu was seated on a tall chair that had curving arms so he could not fall out.

As soon as they were all seated, Mr. Adams bowed his head and said grace. Then he reached for a large slice of corn bread which he spread with homemade butter.

Mrs. Adams, who had been Susanna Boylston of Brookline before her marriage, served the food. She was still a youngish woman, small and buxom, with straight, light brown hair drawn over her ears to a knot at the nape of her neck. Her crisp white caps were always spotless; her calico dresses were often bright and gay.

Now she bent forward to fill the plates with roast pork and potatoes. The thick, brown gravy was promptly passed around. After a few mouthfuls, Mr. John Adams turned to his eldest son, John, and asked his habitual question:

"Well, John, what did you learn in school today?"

It was no idle question. Mr. Adams, like most prosperous farmers of the time, was anxious that his eldest son should go to Harvard and make his mark in the world, preferably as a minister. He remembered that his own father had, at some sacrifice, sent his elder brother Joseph to Harvard. Joseph was now a well-known minister in New Hampshire.

"Father," young John answered rather importantly, "it was what I learned *after* school that matters." And he proceeded to tell how Dame Belcher stacked up many pennies to show how money could be saved to buy land, and how she rolled a coin to show how easily one might get rid of money.

The elder Adams, portly and broad shouldered, smiled at his son.

"There is a woman of common sense for you!" he said earnestly. "Yes, my son, there is real virtue in land. My own farm wasn't so big to start with when my father left it to me. I've been adding land bit by bit, with every penny I could scrape together. Only last month, as you know, I bought the cottage next door and the land that went with it. Today my farm is as fine as most farms hereabouts. Of course I may have to sell a part of it, maybe Stony Acres, to send you to Harvard. But maybe I won't need to. We'll see. We mustn't cross bridges till we come to them."

Young John Adams was silent. It must be a fine thing to go to Harvard, he thought, seeing that so much store was laid by it. Yet, somehow he couldn't picture himself as a minister. He could hardly explain why. He knew his father expected him to become one, and he did not want to hurt his father's feelings. He knew his father had been many things in his time: a shoemaker, a leather expert, a constable, an ensign in the militia, and a deacon in the church.

The elder Adams was in a reminiscent mood. "Our family," he said, "has been here as long as our little town of Braintree. My grandfather, who came from England, was the first Town Clerk here. You might say we have grown up with the town, and the town with us. We work hard, but it's nothing compared to the ordeal our fathers faced before us. They had to build houses, develop the land which was a wilderness, and fight the Indians while they were doing it. The last danger may not be over by any means. Only a dozen or so years ago, when we put up our little wooden church, we also built the stone garrison house to shelter us from the redskins. I dare say," Mr. John Adams smiled ruefully, "we and our neighbors in Boston settled along the sea so that we could take to boats, if we needed to, in the hour of danger."

"We've fought the French a great deal, too, haven't we, Father?" asked young John, taking advantage of a pause, during which his mother briskly removed the plates and passed around ample slices of rhubarb pie.

"We've always been fighting the French," replied his father, balancing a good-sized slice of pie on his knife, "and many a time they incited the Indians against us. At this very moment our own young men, men from Boston and all New England, are laying siege to Louisburg, the fort on the tip of Cape Breton Island. A tough job, but I hope we can teach those Frenchies a lesson!"

Many times young John had heard his father talk about the French hostility to British colonials. So he did not feel at all friendly toward the French. He, like his father, like all the men of Braintree and Boston, was an Englishman. John was filled with pride at the thought.

CHAPTER TWO

THE FRENCH MENACE

EARLY IN JULY 1745 ALL THE BELLS OF BOSTON pealed out jubilantly, as did the bells of Braintree and every town and village in New England.

Victory!

Louisburg, the large French fortress on the tip of Cape Breton Island, had fallen to New England men. The siege had been long and difficult, but at last their unequalled courage had been crowned by victory.

On that hot summer morning young John Adams felt great pride. He could scarcely breathe; tears came to his eyes.

The French, the evil French, had been beaten! Boston was safe! Hostile, foreign men would not land on the Braintree beaches.

There was reason for pride. This great victory had

11

been won, not by the famous forces of His Britannic Majesty, but by colonial troops.

"How well I recall," John's father told the family, "the brave troops as they poured into Boston and out onto the waiting ships that windy day last March. There were ninety transports, I heard, and schooners, too. What a showing of sails it was! I never saw a finer sight. It's one I shall never forget, but my heart misgave me. They were raw, ill-armed lads," his father paused reflectively.

After a minute he resumed, "Now, see, John, what they have done! 'Tis said they've brought back the iron cross from the market place of Louisburg. I'd like to see that cross."

"Oh, so should I!" six-year-old Peter Boylston interrupted his father. "I want to see the soldiers, too."

"The Braintree men will be along soon," his father assured him. "That is, those who can come back," he added in a lower tone, not wishing to diminish the excitement of his young sons. He had heard that more than nine hundred brave men of New England found their graves in the far-off Cape Breton Island.

Again that night and for many nights the bells rang out. Illuminations and fireworks were staged on a grand scale in Boston, but John learned of the excitement at secondhand. Since his father's death, eight-year-old John Hancock had lived in Boston with his uncle, one of the richest men in Massachusetts. Young Hancock rode out with tales to tell which made him the envy of all the lads in Braintree. This was just what John Hancock enjoyed. Wide-eyed he told and retold of the wonderful fireworks, the immense bonfires, the wild cheering as more and more soldiers returned to Boston.

Young John Adams was not to see John Hancock again until they met at Harvard College, where Hancock, though younger, was in a class ahead of John.

A little over a year later, in the early autumn, the excitement in Braintree again rose to a high pitch. But this time it was not the pleasurable excitement caused by a great victory. On the contrary, it was an agitation aroused by fear, fear of the French vengeance. The French had been enraged when Louisburg fell. So they fitted up a marvelous fleet of ships and set sail for the New World.

That October day young John Adams stood alone on top of the hill from which he could see Boston to the northward. The stone was cold beneath his bare feet; he curled his toes and tried to shield his eyes with his hand, as the northeast wind, blowing down from Cape Sable, made his flesh tingle.

It was this wind from the northeast that made Boston's situation so immediately critical. For a week past, the wind had blown from the southeast and Boston had been safe from the terrible oncoming French fleet. For no ship bearing down from Cape Sable could gain entrance into Boston's harbor.

Over the bright reds, yellows, and browns of autumn trees the bay of Boston spread blue and clear on that October morning. John's father had said that this dangerous wind would last three days, three days and three nights in which the enemy fleet could make the harbor safely and burn Boston to the ground.

Then the fleet could come down to Braintree and burn the Adams farm, as well as everything else in its path. John knew the Frenchies planned just this. Hadn't Dame Belcher herself talked to him about the danger of soldiers landing on the Braintree beaches?

Just the night before, when the wind had changed, the men of Braintree and Dame Belcher had met in his father's kitchen, the kitchen which had sheltered the Adamses for generations, where the beams along the ceiling and the windows were already black with age.

That night John had crept to the door and listened.

"The French didn't frighten my father nor my father's father out of Braintree," John had heard his father say in his assured, resonant voice. "The French were here the year I was born, back in 1691. They got as far as York, burning and killing. They had Indians with them that trip. It was winter and they used snowshoes. A cousin of my father's saw the Indians. We fought the French again when I was twenty."

He paused. John knew his father was turning his penetrating eyes from one person to another. "I'm here now, alive and well. So are you, and you, and you!"

Whom was he singling out? John wondered. Probably the men who had urged the village to pack up and move to safety. Yes, it must be those men, young John decided, though he could hear no one reply.

His father's voice went on. He was speaking louder and more vigorously than before:

"Am I to pack up now and run away, just because a French fleet has been sighted some four hundred miles to eastward?"

Young John had shivered with cold during the ensuing silence. He didn't want to leave the farm. Why, the farm was part of himself! It would be like cutting himself in two and leaving half behind; the better half, he knew, for it was the better half of him that felt close to the farm.

Suddenly the thought of leaving the Braintree farm frightened young John Adams far more than the thought of the oncoming French fleet.

"I'll be here to take in my apple crop," his father's calm voice broke the silence, "unless the French get here first and cut down my trees."

There was a scraping of chairs. Dame Belcher spoke vigorously in her aged, cracked voice, but John could not catch her words. He did not need to hear what the others said. He knew they agreed with his father. He felt more proud of his father than ever before. He was a great man, a leader of the men of Braintree!

Of course, he was! Wasn't he the head of the local militia? Wasn't the powder barrel stored right down below the barn?

This morning, up on the top of the hill, John remembered all that. He shaded his eyes against the wind and peered into the blue haze.

There was no sight of ship or enemy.

Yet the danger remained imminent for three days. His father had said so that very morning, when he told how in the Old South Meeting House in Boston they had prayed on Sunday for deliverance:

" 'Send us Thy tempest, Lord, upon the waters to the eastward. Raise Thy right hand. Scatter the ships of our tormentors and drive them hence. Sink their proud frigates beneath the power of Thy winds.'

"It was then," his father went on, "the winds

shrieked, sudden and tempestuous, and whistled around the corners of the old church, pounding against the windows. And the great bell of the church struck twice."

It was the Lord's voice answering the frightened believers, young John was sure. He begged his father to repeat the story. It gave him courage. Peter Boylston stared wide eyed when his father told of the

strange ringing of the bell. It was a miracle, everyone in Braintree said.

Such a week as that one in October 1746 young John could never forget. The wind changed and blew from the north down from Cape Sable, leaving Boston open to the enemy. The tar barrel still stood unlighted on top of Beacon Hill when news of the French fleet reached Boston: d'Anville, the great French admiral, was dead! Slain by his own hand, some whispered, so great was his despair when he saw his men dying with scurvy and fevers. Two thousand men had been buried at sea, four thousand were sick to death on board. Two of the largest French frigates had been sunk in the storm. The vice-admiral had run his own sword through his heart. The few remaining ships were trying to reach the safety of the West Indies.

The Lord had indeed answered, and the people of Braintree gathered that Sunday in the Congregational Church to render thanksgiving where it was due.

"If God is with us, who can be against us?" the minister asked.

A most reasonable question, young John thought. And he suddenly felt much better than he had felt for weeks.

CHAPTER THREE

AN EXCITING DAY

YOUNG JOHN MANAGED TO CONJUGATE THE END-less Latin words, but more than half of his mind was on the French disaster. Soon Mr. Cleverly, master of the local Free Latin School, became aware of John's inattention. Promptly John was assigned a double lesson to stimulate his interest!

Two lessons of the hated language! John kicked the road so fiercely, as he walked home, that his toes were bruised. It felt fine to have bruised toes. That was something he could understand.

He hastened to the barn and pressed his head against the warm hide of the patient cows as he did his customary milking. He loved animals. Why must he go to the hateful Latin School? If college was anything like this, he wanted no college either, he decided.

18

John had been so happy and done so well with Dame Belcher that his mother had allowed him to linger there beyond the usual age. Since the change of schools, she had worried about him. He seemed listless. He no longer chatted on his return from school; he no longer sang as he worked. This quietness disturbed her.

After this state of affairs had gone on for a year, and John had made little or no progress in the Latin School and become more and more quiet at home, she took up the matter with his father one night.

On that particular day John had played truant. He had remained away from home until long after time for milking. He had never missed doing his farm chores before, not in all his half dozen years of useful boyhood.

It had been a day young John Adams would never forget. A day full of another kind of education, very unlike that which Mr. Cleverly dispensed.

He had started out in the chill of that November morning as he did every day. But when he neared the Latin School, everything in him rebelled. He turned suddenly, without thinking, and ran as fast as he could up the Coast Road toward Boston. He ran until he was completely winded. Only then did he stop by the roadside to rest. As he sat there in the cold, a horse approached, drawing a cart with produce for the Boston market. John recognized a neighbor, even as he was recognized in turn. The horse was slowed to a stop.

"Well, if it isn't young John Adams!" exclaimed Mr. Newcomb. "What are you doing here?"

John arose and came to the side of the cart. "Would you take me to Boston with you?" he asked anxiously.

Mr. Newcomb was a jolly young man and inclined to give any youngster a lift; but he hesitated. "Shouldn't you be in school? It seems to me I heard you were attending Mr. Cleverly's Latin School."

The color rose to young John Adams' face. But he looked squarely at his neighbor.

"Maybe I ought to be there, but I'm not! I hate Latin!"

These words were spoken with such fervor as to cause Mr. Newcomb to break into loud guffaws.

At the sound of his laughter, John hoisted himself up onto the seat, well aware that Mr. Newcomb would take him to Boston.

For some miles neither spoke. The only sound was the steady thump of the horse's hooves and the cart wheels on the frozen road. The trees were nearly leafless; a wind blew up from the sea, smelling of fish.

As they approached Boston, they sighted the huge fleet in the harbor.

"Could be you came in to welcome Commodore Knowles to our shores?" Mr. Newcomb smiled at John, then he frowned and said, "It may be dangerous around the wharves, you know. The press gangs are out, I heard tell."

"I'm an Englishman," John replied proudly. "I have no fear of His Majesty's sailors."

"Ho, my lad, I've heard pride goes before a fall," Mr. Newcomb looked gravely at John. "I wouldn't want you to disappear and have to explain myself to your father."

"There's no danger of that," John said crisply. "I can take care of myself."

"Let's hope you can." Mr. Newcomb's voice still sounded doubtful as he turned his horse down Brattle Street, past King Street toward the Long Wharf. "If I let you out here will you meet me before dark, right down by the Town House?"

"That I will," promised John, his eyes shining with excitement. "Never fear. I have money for lunch." He proudly displayed the few pennies he had in his pocket.

"Now look out for those sailors, John Adams," warned Mr. Newcomb as he waved good-by.

John skipped along down King Street, his eyes turning this way and that. To his right lay ships from all the ports in the world, while out in the bay were anchored the fine vessels of His Majesty's Navy, back from Louisburg.

The Long Wharf was like a street, for on the left were rows of shops and houses. Great sea gulls were circling round and round overhead; now and again one would alight and cling with huge feet to a wharf post or roof edge.

John passed a group of jolly sailors dressed in blue uniforms, striped jerseys, and cocked hats. How grand they looked, thought John. He felt so happy he began to hum his favorite hymn:

"'O give ye thanks unto the Lord,
Because that good is He . . .'"

What a fine thing to be an Englishman!
Suddenly he saw another crowd of six or seven sail-

ors. They were dragging two boys toward a boat which was docked at one end of the Long Wharf. The boys were struggling and screaming.

"Help! Help!" John heard them cry.

One of the boys broke away from the men and leaped from the dock into the cold gray sea. Heads appeared in the various windows.

The door of one of the shops was flung open. A woman ran out.

"Press gang! Press gang!" she screamed. Then she spied John.

"You are a stranger," she said softly. "Get away as fast as you can. Those British sailors are evil men."

John couldn't believe his ears nor his own eyes. He turned, but coming toward him were three rough-looking sailors armed with stout clubs.

A sense of self-preservation came to the boy just in time. He dodged toward the shops and edged between two small houses. In desperation he tried a door he found on one side. It was unlatched, and he entered.

None too soon. He heard a violent knocking on a door facing the wharf. The shop bell tinkled; the door opened just as he managed to hide behind a box which stood in front of an open closet.

A woman's steps sounded on the stairs.

"What can I do for you?" John heard her ask.

"We're looking for a lad who dodged in here," a gruff voice replied.

"Not in here," the woman said stoutly. "You have the wrong shop."

"I know this woman," another sailor said. "She is telling the truth. Let's look in the shop next door. It is likely the boy is there. The woman who owns it was screaming a while ago."

Apparently the sailors were undecided. After a few minutes, however, the footsteps retreated and John heard the door close after them. He was, by then, too frightened to move.

"Come out of there, my lad," the lady called softly, "and be quick about it. Those sailors will be back any time. Get upstairs and take your shoes off and hide them under the bed. Pull the covers up to your chin and breathe softly. I'll handle them."

The strange woman spoke kindly, but she looked grim and determined. John could not imagine how she knew he had been hiding there.

He mounted the stairs as softly and rapidly as he could, and obeyed her instructions. Breathe softly, John repeated to himself as he pulled off his boots; his fingers seemed all thumbs, so great was his haste. Breathe softly. Could he breathe at all?

He half hid his face and began repeating to himself another verse, a comforting verse, of the hymn he'd joyously started to sing when he reached the Long Wharf a few minutes before. A few minutes? It had seemed to John like hours!

> " 'Then did they to Jehovah cry,
>   When they were in distress;
>   Who did set them at liberty
>   Out of their anguish . . .' "

The familiar words comforted him. And he was in need of comfort, for he heard the men returning!

"There's no lad next door," the sailor's gruff voice

sounded far gruffer to John's straining ears. "Now, Madam, with your leave, or without it, we shall search here!"

"That's as you please," he heard the woman reply lightly. "But I should warn you my niece is here with the smallpox. You'll find nothing but death if you go to her room."

"The pox!" the gruff voice sounded frightened. "Let's get out of here, men!"

"Why didn't you tell us this before?" John heard another sailor demand suspiciously.

"You didn't ask me," the woman replied briskly. She seemed indifferent. "I don't advertise it, you know."

"I shall warn my friends away from this shop," the man said.

"That's as you please," the woman retorted. "I must be going to the doctor again presently. My niece is really bad."

When the sailors had left, the woman came up to John.

"I told but the truth, my lad," she said with a twinkle in her eyes. "You are bad. You don't belong hereabouts. You look like a country boy. You should have stayed at home in dangerous times."

"But those were English sailors. I never thought English sailors would hurt me." John could not get over his bewilderment.

"Have you never heard of press gangs, boy?"

John admitted he had, but somehow it had seemed very different when he heard the stories, safe on the Braintree farm. He tried to explain this to the kind woman.

"Now get your boots on," she said. "When it's dusk

we'll try to get you back into town, though there may still be a barricade even then."

Until dusk, the solid barricade erected by the sailors permitted them to continue their impressment, undisturbed by the aroused Bostonians.

Bells began to ring soon after John drew on his boots. They grew louder and louder. The crowds grew larger and larger on King Street. There were angry shouts on every side, mingling with the cries and screams of the men who had been trapped. It was horrible. Five or six grown men with clubs against one young apprentice. John had never imagined Englishmen would act in this cowardly way.

As the bells rang on, the crowd on the wharf grew larger. The press gangs were frightened off by the mob, which surged to the water's edge and shook angry fists at the retreating barges.

Worn out with excitement and fright, John managed to get through the crowds to the Town House. Soon he recognized Mr. Newcomb and his now-empty cart. John's heart leapt with joy at the familiar, friendly sight of his neighbor.

"Why, you're tuckered out," young Mr. Newcomb said with concern. He took the blanket from the horse and spread it on the floor of the cart. "Lie down here and sleep. We'll be back in Braintree in no time," he said cheerfully.

The jouncing of the cart, vigorous as it was, did not keep the tired boy from sleep. John was dreaming of jumping into the sea to escape pursuers when he awoke with a start to find himself in front of his own home.

His father greeted him grimly. Usually John didn't

mind a caning, but this night he felt it was unjust.
Perhaps Latin and Greek at Mr. Cleverly's were not
the worst things in the world, John thought as he
slowly mounted the stairs and flung his exhausted
body into his own bed.

The woman who had befriended him had thrust
some coins into his hands when she bade him good-by.
In the morning he found them on the floor beside his
bed. He looked at them curiously. He had never before seen a Portuguese joe or a Spanish piece of eight.
The nightmare was over, but here was proof that it
had been real.

For a year or more he attended the Latin School,
becoming month by month more quiet and unhappy.
His father had refused to consider his leaving the
school. Mr. Adams had set his heart on sending his
oldest son to Harvard College.

When the news came that a treaty had been signed
and that England had given Louisburg back to the
French, the people of Boston and Braintree were as
irate and bewildered as John himself had been after
his experiences on the Long Wharf.

CHAPTER FOUR

LATIN OR DIGGING DITCHES?

O NE DAY JOHN WAS SO DISGUSTED, TRYING TO conjugate endless words, that he burst out in class.

"What is the use of Latin?" he asked Mr. Cleverly.

"If you haven't learned that after four years in my school, you will never know," replied Mr. Cleverly coldly.

John was momentarily abashed. His face reddened. He heard a snicker from the boy behind him.

This aroused his anger. Mr. Cleverly had not answered cleverly at all, he thought to himself. Mr. Cleverly was not a clever man, or he would not ridicule an honest question. John became more and more angry as he buried his face deeper in the hated book.

When class was dismissed he hurried home even faster than usual. His father had given him a young colt and he was impatient to ride him. Ride him he did, and his anger at Latin verbs was forgotten in the joy of his freedom. He cantered over the fields and up and down the rutty roads until dark.

He was late for supper, but no one chided him. Peter Boylston was able to help now, and even young Elihu could assist with the milking.

Several days later, when John was playing rounders with his friends, he observed Mr. Cleverly in conversation with his father. John felt uncomfortable and missed the ball, something he rarely did.

He was very quiet that evening. The next day he went fishing with his uncle. He loved to fish and hunt with the older members of the family. Any outdoor task was a pleasure to young John, just as confinement in school was painful, even without the additional horror of those endless Latin words. He returned triumphantly with the largest fish of the catch and heard his uncle say to his father:

"John's a grown man. Why, he can outfish me!"

"He may be able to catch bigger fish than you, but Mr. Cleverly tells me his Latin shows no improvement," retorted his father crisply. "In fact, he cannot pass John to the higher class."

"I *hate* Latin!" John shouted loudly.

His uncle burst into a roaring laugh, but his father was very quiet. He did not reply to his son, but turned and entered the house.

After dinner, when John started upstairs, his father called him back: "Sit down here with your mother and me. We must talk with you about your lack of interest in the Free Latin School."

"How can I be interested in dull conjugations?" John

demanded. "We never read or do anything interesting there."

"You go to be taught, not to criticize, my son," his father said gravely. "How can you enter Harvard College if you do not study?"

"I don't want to go to Harvard College if I've got to keep on with Latin. I *hate* it. I'd rather work on the farm all my life."

"Fine!" He knew by the tone of his father's voice

that he was very angry and unhappy. "If Latin grammar does not suit you, you may try ditching. My meadow yonder is in need of a ditch. You may start early in the morning. Perhaps that will better satisfy you."

This seemed to John a delightful change. So next morning he gaily hastened to the meadow. But he found ditching far harder than Latin. That morning was the longest that he had ever experienced. By dinnertime he was exhausted. It would have been impossible to talk. His one desire was to get to bed and to sleep.

Yet when he was in bed he found he could not sleep. His mind turned from the advantages and disadvantages of Latin, to digging ditches and back again. Back and forth the problem went, even in his fitful dreams.

The next morning John returned to the ditch. He had scarcely spoken to his mother, father, or brothers. Throughout the forenoon his shovel was never idle. By dinnertime John wanted to return to Latin grammar. This was a humiliating predicament. He found himself tongue-tied.

So he returned and dug again at the meadow ditch. John dug and dug until his back ached and his hands were blistered. He found he was more angry with himself than with his father. Yet he was determined to finish the job. Each hour seemed far longer than the one before, as he stubbornly dug on. By the time the sun finally reached the horizon, his dislike of the toil conquered his boyish pride.

Haltingly he approached his father.

"If you choose to have me, I will go back to Latin

grammar," John said, his eyes downcast. He rubbed his bare feet together and waited.

Old John Adams looked long and solemnly at his humiliated young son.

"You're a big man now, John," he observed gravely. "You'll have to take life seriously. There's to be no more time spent at rounders, no more fishing parties, no long rambles through the marshes and woods. You are already behind other boys of your age."

"Yes, sir," agreed John miserably. Without another word he turned and slowly climbed the steep stairs to his chamber. He fell asleep as soon as his head touched the bed. His sleep was troubled with night-mares, for he dreamed he was drowning in ditches because Mr. Cleverly held him under the dirty water!

The next morning his mother called him to her side and made a suggestion which changed everything:

"I've been thinking, John, that the way Mr. Cleverly teaches may not be a good way for you. I talked to Dame Belcher about it, and to your father. Your father says if Mr. Marsh will take you, you need not go back to the Free Latin School."

"You mean I can go to Mr. Marsh's tutoring school?" Suddenly John felt exuberant. "Will he teach me so I can go to Harvard, as Father wants?"

He recalled the shabby old house where Mr. Marsh taught his pupils, with the playing field behind where John had often seen laughing lads kicking a football about.

Mrs. Adams took up her sewing and smiled at her excited son. "Yes, John, if Mr. Marsh will take you, you may go there. Go and ask him," she urged.

Faster than he had ever run, even in a game of rounders, John tore out of the house. The stiff, painful muscles were forgotten. He fairly galloped up the road to the old Marsh house. A wide-spreading buttonwood tree shaded the front steps, but there was no sign of the schoolmaster.

John felt suddenly shy. What if Mr. Marsh would not take him into his school? He turned slowly toward the back yard, where during holidays he had often seen the schoolmaster reading under a tree. Perhaps he would be there now.

Sure enough, the long, thin figure was stretched on its stomach, bending over a book. Mr. Marsh looked up at the boy's approach and waved to him.

As John drew near he saw it was Cicero's *Letters to Atticus* which the schoolmaster was reading.

"Good morning, John," he greeted the boy pleasantly. "What can I do for you?"

When John, somewhat breathless, made no reply, the schoolmaster rose to a sitting position and patted the ground at his side.

"Sit down here and tell me about it," he suggested.

In no time at all John was pouring all his difficulties into the sympathetic ear. He smiled ruefully as he told of his recent ditching in the meadow.

"My father says that I am already a man," John ended his tale. "He wants me to be in Harvard within a year."

"*Ferocitas iuvenum* . . ." Mr. Marsh stopped and looked quizzically at John. "Do you know what that means?"

"The impetuosity of youth . . ." John grinned. He

tried to reply in Latin, but his tongue refused to help him out. Instead he said: "My mother says I may come to your school if you can get me into Harvard College next year."

"And your father? Does he desire it?" Mr. Marsh asked, adding, "I am no Atticus to be friends of both sides in civil war."

John was embarrassed. He knew his father did not like Mr. Marsh. Perhaps he couldn't understand the schoolmaster. And John himself didn't know exactly what he meant about Atticus and civil war.

"My father desires more than anything that I go to Harvard College," John said solemnly. "If you can teach me enough to pass the entrance examinations, he will be satisfied."

"Oh, I'll have you in Harvard within twelve months, Johnny, never fear." Mr. Marsh spoke with such assurance that John felt tears coming to his eyes.

"You may tell your father that," Mr. Marsh said cheerily, "and come here next Monday morning."

It was not long before John discovered that he must work harder at Mr. Marsh's tutoring school than he had ever worked at the Free Latin School.

But no true New Englander ever feared hard work. John studied Latin and rhetoric with a new will. He mastered them for the sake of kind, quizzical Mr. Marsh. He could not have worked any harder or with greater zest. He was determined that his father should not blame Joseph Marsh for his failure. Not that John thought he would fail. He said to himself, he could not fail, he must not fail.

That year he was the only boy from Braintree to go

up to Harvard for the examinations. The others came from neighboring towns, from Weymouth or Dorchester, or from boarding schools as far away as Worcester.

On the fateful day, Friday, July 6, 1751, a mist hung over the Braintree marshes. John dressed himself in his very best blue suit with metal buttons. His linen was spotless. As soon as breakfast was over he saddled his mare, a gift from his father who was much pleased at his progress.

John trotted down the road to the old Marsh house. The schoolmaster had promised to go in with him and introduce him to President Holyoke and the college tutors. They planned to spend the night in Boston.

To John's surprise old Mrs. Marsh opened the door to him. She explained that her son was in bed with a severe attack of the gout.

John was aghast. He stood there silently. He could say nothing.

"You'll have to go alone," the old lady informed him. "It'll be a good thing for you, boy. We all are alone always. The sooner we get over depending on anyone but ourselves the better. Get along, lad, and pass those examinations as Joseph has prepared you to do. Be a credit to my boy, and you'll do more to cure him than I can."

Still John said nothing. He just stared at her.

Mrs. Marsh gave him a gentle push.

"You know the way to Boston, John," she insisted. "Anyone can direct you to Harvard College. Now hasten along, or you'll be late."

John remounted his mare as if in a dream. Luckily the slender animal was headed in the right direction.

For some minutes John scarcely knew where he was.

How could he face all those strangers alone? Where would he eat? Where sleep? How make himself clean and presentable after the long ride?

He had no difficulty in finding Harvard Hall, where he mounted the steps slowly and hesitatingly. At last he found himself in a large room with benches against the walls. Boys of various ages were sitting there, waiting.

At one end of the room a man in a scholar's gown was at a high desk, writing. He looked up when John entered, and told him to wait his turn with the other boys.

John's eyes went roving over his companions in misery. There were eighteen young men waiting with him. He had just finished counting them when a side door opened and another man in a scholar's gown emerged.

The boy nearest the door arose and disappeared. Soon John's turn would come. Would he pass? His heart beat so fast it almost choked him. He hugged his cocked hat more tightly under his arm. He wished he had taken time to shine his coat buttons and shoe buckles. They looked dull and dusty to his critical eye. What if the tutors would not examine him? Would they consider him too shabby?

The boy next to him suddenly leaned over and asked him in a whisper how old he was.

"Fifteen," John answered.

"I'm only twelve," the other said.

Twelve, John repeated to himself. No wonder his father had thought him too old! What if he failed and this twelve-year-old passed? The imagined humiliation made his cheeks flush a fiery red.

His turn had come. He could scarcely stand. His feet felt like wads of rubber. Somehow, he would never know how, he managed to reach the side doorway and pass through.

He entered a square room, panelled in shining walnut, lined with handsome portraits. What a beautiful room, John thought. Then he raised his eyes to meet those of the finest-looking man he had ever seen, dressed in a black silk robe, his head surmounted by a handsome wig. It was President Holyoke. He bowed to John.

"Adams, is it? John Adams?" the President's voice rang overloud in John's frightened ears. "Where do you live?"

Scarcely above a whisper, John murmured, "Braintree."

"Braintree! It must be your father I've heard Colonel Quincy speak of. I think you have cousins who graduated here."

Before he could collect his amazed thoughts, a tutor addressed him in Latin. His confidence had been restored when the President said he knew his father and uncle. He replied easily in good Latin. Mr. Marsh had primed him for this joke of the old tutor. He had not been caught unawares.

Next came a question in rhetoric. John could not answer it, but no one seemed to mind.

Another scholar then gave him a long paper written in English and told him to put it into Latin. John remembered the catalogue which he had learned by heart.

He had long known he would be asked "extempore to read, construe, and parse Tully or Virgil and to write good Latin prose and be skilled in making nice Latin verses, or at least in the rules of Prosodia; also to read, construe, and parse ordinary Greek, as in the New Testament and Isocrates, and to decline the paradigms of Greek nouns and verbs."

So first came the Latin, which troubled him less than he had expected. The scholar took him to a quiet corner and offered a dictionary. He informed him he knew Mr. Marsh very well.

"Take your time, Adams," he cautioned John. "It does not pay to hurry."

When the day was done and he returned home in the dusky twilight, tired but excited, he knew that he had passed. Now his father would be pleased. In his heart, young John Adams resolved that evening that his father should one day be very proud of him.

HARVARD COLLEGE

B OY!" THE LOUD CALL PURSUED JOHN ADAMS, AS QUI-
etly, almost on tiptoe, his plump legs glided
down the long corridor to his dormitory in Massachusetts Hall.

"Boy!" the cry was repeated, just as John was about
to turn the corner toward the stairway.

In the strange new world which was Harvard,
young John Adams, who valued his independence,
hated this custom called "fagging." Fagging had been
brought over from England; it was a custom that permitted an upper classman to order a freshman about,
and even to ask him to perform some menial task.

"Yes?" John replied, retracing his footsteps and un-
willingly coming to the door from which a vain sophomore stuck his head.

39

"Say 'Yes, sir,'" insisted the sophomore, much to John's annoyance.

"Yes, sir," John repeated after him, boiling inside with rage and hiding it the best he knew how.

It irked him all the more because the student who addressed him, although a sophomore, was actually two years younger than he. John was then sixteen. By what right did the sophomore call him "Boy"? John had difficulty controlling his mounting irritation.

He knew, of course, that when he became a sophomore, he in his turn could call a freshman "Boy" and order him about just as this fellow was doing. But already John had made up his mind that he would never do that, that he would never do anything to make another boy in a similar position feel this loss of personal dignity. He didn't like what was being done to him; why should he do the same thing to another?

"Yes, sir," he repeated, this time with a sense of pride which would have made a more sensitive boy than the sophomore squirm.

"That's better," said the bossy sophomore, with an effort to rub it in. "Boy," he went on, "will you go downstairs and ask my friend in the room just below mine to let you have the sand box for blotting the paper."

"Yes," said John Adams, who by this time was amused. What a lot of fuss over a little sand box! John's natural cheerfulness had reasserted itself and he galloped happily to the floor below.

It had not taken him long to discover it is better not to fight custom, however unjust. Someone had explained to him that fagging taught young men obedience and humility. Young as he was, John had sensibly decided that there must be some better way of teaching these things.

Yet he reasoned to himself that if other freshmen put up with fagging, why shouldn't he? He could and did, but his pride and independence were increased by this, rather than his obedience and humility!

Here at Harvard College, where three large buildings enclosed three sides of the Yard, John felt confined. To be sure, the Cambridge Common and the succession of meadows where the professors' houses were situated gave it a country air. But it was far different from Braintree, if not much larger.

John missed the fields and woods of Braintree; the fishing, the hunting, the long aimless rambles through the meadows and along the familiar seashore. He missed, too, the hayloft where he had sometimes studied his Latin grammar. What a pity, he thought, that he was not permitted to possess a gun. The fields and woods in the neighborhood of Cambridge abounded in game.

The students were not even allowed outside of the college grounds unless they wore their gowns. For the most part they were expected to stay in their rooms and pursue their studies diligently. This was particularly hard for an outdoor boy such as John Adams.

Luckily the college was only ten miles from Braintree. The rules permitted four days each month to be spent with his family. During the summer he was granted a six weeks' vacation. At such times ball and bat resounded as John played rounders with his brothers and their friends. Once more there were exhilarating gallops on his favorite colt; once more there were delightful hunting and fishing expeditions; again he could ramble through the familiar meadows and woods. It was good to be home.

Here in Braintree he was able to forget the inequalities practiced at Harvard College, where the boys were graded not according to individual merit and accomplishment, but according to the social and financial standing of their families.

His childhood friend, John Hancock, was at Harvard, too, but he was in the class ahead of John. Forgetful of his modest beginnings, before he fell heir to his uncle's fortune, John Hancock ostentatiously displayed a wardrobe which contained many elegant suits, choice hats, and several pairs of shoes, besides finely finished shirts of every description, ruffled, pleated, and even lace-edged. One of Hancock's friends had so many shirts, hats, and shoes that John could not help saying to his mother:

"Why, Mother, he had so many things he could easily open a shop with them!"

"Don't be envious, John," his mother admonished him.

He still remembered the opening day in August when his father had brought him to college, his clothes and his bedding in a farm cart. They stopped in front of the Yard just at the moment when a carriage drawn by four fine horses came up behind, bringing a richly attired boy.

Will I fit in here? John had wondered that day. Yet later he had not minded so much. After all, he had come to Harvard College to study, not to display fine clothes. His father had sacrificed to send him; indeed, he had to sell Stony Acres to do it. John remembered, too, his father's parting words:

"John, I am bringing you here, a farmer's boy. I expect you to depart from here four years hence a minister of the gospel. I want you to study diligently, behave like a gentleman, live up to the expectations of your mother and your father."

With these words, spoken in a grave voice, he had left his son. Young John was painfully conscious of the responsibility thrust upon him, yet he again found himself wondering if he wanted to be a clergyman.

For a few moments he had stood as one lost, that first day at Harvard. Then he had straightened his shoulders, as his eyes followed the slender, elegantly dressed young man who stepped from the carriage and entered the Yard as if it were the grounds of his own home. The liveried driver followed, carrying endless boxes.

Ambitious and proud as young John Adams was, a wild idea had come into his mind at that moment. He resolved to surpass in studies. In spite of his few plain clothes and humble appearance, his demeanor should be beyond reproach. He had read in Bacon's *Essays* that "Manners maketh the man."

To his delight he discovered on the shelves of the college library, which contained some four thousand volumes, some dramatic classics. John eagerly pounced on these. Throughout his second and third years he read them avidly. What a huge library it was, he often thought, probably the largest in America! How lucky he was to have it at his disposal.

He particularly liked the tragedies. One evening he read the "Agamemnon" of the Greek poet and dramatist, Aeschylus, before the Discussion Club to which he had recently been elected. He read with such warmth and expression as to delight the members. It caused one of them to ask him afterward:

"Did you say you were studying for the ministry? Why, from the way you read that old play I'd say you were better fitted to become an actor, or, at any rate, a lawyer!"

John was beginning to find himself, which also meant that others were beginning to find him. He was making friends. What a pleasure it was to be among them and exchange ideas! He found in his contact with new friends some compensation for the loss of Braintree, which he still missed.

One evening toward the end of his third year he and his two closest friends were enjoying a last talk before graduation. Both Sam Quincy and Daniel Treadwell were a year ahead of John. This was the last time these three would be together as students.

"Old Winthrop did himself proud today, didn't he?" Treadwell's enthusiasm shone in his eyes as well as in his excited voice.

"Yes," agreed Quincy, "it was a fine thing he maintained—that a man may believe in God and eternal life and still work for the advancement of science, if that is where his personal bent lies."

"Exactly," said Treadwell, who was considered the most alert young man in the college. "It used to be that the theologians objected to science on the ground that a little learning in that direction robs men of their religious beliefs. But Mr. Winthrop sensibly holds that the more we know of the work of God in the creation of the universe, the more we are likely to glorify His name. Really, what else is a telescope but something which teaches us of the marvels of heaven?"

His eyes glowing with enthusiasm, Treadwell added: "Whatever anyone says, the world *does* move. Nothing can stop it from moving. I, for one, believe an era of science is dawning!"

Treadwell's voice had a warmth that impressed his hearers; it had a confident quality that made them believe him. Similarly they believed Professor Winthrop, who presented his facts in such a way as to convey the meaning of the new physical forces.

"What do you think our divinity professor, Wigglesworth, will say to all this?" asked John Adams.

"What could he say?" Treadwell answered. "After all, Professor Winthrop's remarks do not contradict any belief in God."

"I hear Benjamin Franklin is doing great things in Philadelphia," put in Sam Quincy.

"Well, I should say so," said Treadwell. "Professor Winthrop spoke of him only the other day. They are friends, I understand. Franklin, it seems, has been making experiments with electricity. He's discovered that lightning and electricity are the same thing. He has suggested that lightning rods might be erected to protect buildings from destruction. Just think of it!" Treadwell exclaimed with excitement, "it all started with his flying a kite! A little thing like that, and yet what results!"

John Adams broke in with pride: "Franklin went to Philadelphia from Boston!"

"Yes, it is strange how such things so often lead to bigger things," drawled Sam Quincy, resuming the thread of the conversation.

"You know, Treadwell," said John, "you'd make a wonderful teacher. You seem to be able to convey things to others and make people believe them."

"That's exactly what I intend to be—a teacher!" said Treadwell.

"And I'm going to be a lawyer." Quincy laughed then added, "We—the three of us—are going to be the pillars of society. Treadwell a teacher, I a lawyer, and you, Adams, I believe, are going to be a minister."

John suddenly felt abashed. Was he really going to be a minister? He was not sure. The matter troubled him. He would like to please his father. Yet he felt he might want to be something else. He envied Treadwell and Sam Quincy, who were both so sure of what they wanted and intended to be.

"I don't know," he murmured with a shyness unusual to him.

He had at least a year to decide, while his two friends were graduating this year.

It was a gala day, a year later, when John graduated with twenty-three others. The grounds around Harvard College looked like a country fair. Tents and booths were all around the Yard. Jugglers and conjurers, acrobats and clowns were performing. Fiddlers were strumming, children were skipping, young people were dancing. There were even Indians with their paint and feathers.

For days before Commencement vehicles came pouring in, among them fine coaches carrying smartly dressed passengers. Clouds of dust rose from the roads. The inns were full. The visitors, and the stu-

dents as well, spent their money wildly. There was
some fighting, too. Little crowds collected, laughing
and merrymaking. Harvard College, always so serious
and sedate, did not look like itself. The students, long
kept in by severe discipline, broke loose with noise and
fury. At night it was a curious sight to see people
sleeping under trees. Since it was the second week in
July they were not too uncomfortable.

Early on Friday, the day of Commencement, the
Adams family arrived. There must have been at least
a dozen Adamses there, including John's younger
brothers, Peter and Elihu. For that matter, great
crowds arrived from Braintree.

The elder John Adams, dressed in a new coat with a
white collar, new buckled shoes, and even a cocked
hat, felt stiff and uncomfortable, especially since it
was a warm day. He was too used to the ease of his
farmer's attire. Holding himself rigidly, he consoled
himself with the fact that after his arduous efforts and
sacrifices he would at last see his boy graduate from
Harvard!

It was a comforting thought. In his mind's eye he
saw a vision of John in the pulpit of a church, speaking with an eloquence more persuasive than that of his
own elder brother, Joseph. What if he did sell Stony
Acres to get his boy through college! He would sell ten
farms to achieve the pleasure he was experiencing
now. His own oldest son a minister!

He glanced at his wife, Susanna, who walked with
a soft grace at his side. Why, she looked as cool as you
please, in her handsome beribboned costume and her
new high bonnet. How could she look so calm on such

a day as this, when their boy was going to graduate? Women were curious creatures, he thought.

There was the sound of music. The Governor, escorted by local troops, passed by on the way to church, where the Commencement exercises would take place.

To the tolling of the bell in the steeple, the Adamses crowded into the church with other fathers and mothers, the women ascending to the gallery especially reserved for them.

Then the graduating students, walking in pairs, entered through the door and marched up the aisle to their assigned seats in front. Presently, President Holyoke and other dignitaries took their places on the platform.

As each student mounted the stage, President Holyoke addressed him in Latin. This gave much pleasure to the parents, even though they did not understand a word of Latin. But their sons did, and that delighted them.

Mr. John Adams sat breathless, his excitement growing more intense as he waited for his son's turn. When John finally did appear and replied to President Holyoke's Latin in the same tongue, Mr. Adams was so proud that he could not have uttered a word if he had tried. But Mrs. Adams, in the gallery, in response to the congratulations of her neighbor, murmured almost matter-of-factly:

"Of course! I expected it. My John is a clever boy!"

As for John himself, when he rejoined his parents out-of-doors, he was thinking:

"I hope Father doesn't ask if I'm ready at once to accept a call to the ministry. For heaven knows, if one were now offered me I am not sure that I would!"

For the time being, however, he was spared the question. But he knew that sooner or later it would be asked, and that sooner or later he would have to come to a decision.

CHAPTER SIX

WORCESTER, MASSACHUSETTS

IT WAS A HOT DAY IN JULY, A FEW DAYS AFTER Commencement. The excitement of that event had worn off. John Adams was in his room, in his shirt sleeves. Looking out of the window to catch the slight breeze that came from the sea, he was trying to think out his problem: how to earn a livelihood after the sacrifices his father had made to get him through Harvard.

Suddenly there was a knock on the door. His mother, usually so calm and restrained, rushed into his room, breathless and excited.

"John," she said in a hurried whisper, "slip a coat on quickly! The Reverend Mr. Thaddeus Maccarty, from the church in Worcester, wants to see you. I do hope it has something to do with your becoming a minister!"

50

If Mrs. Adams expected an excited response from her son, she was disappointed.

"I'll be ready in a minute," he said simply, unrolling his sleeves and donning his coat.

He went about this slowly and deliberately. It sounded as though he had prospects. But as he had not yet made up his mind about his future career, he didn't know whether to feel happy or not.

Presently he entered the parlor, where his visitor awaited him. The latter introduced himself, and when they were both seated he stated his errand.

"I was present at the Commencement the other day," Reverend Maccarty began, "and heard you answer President Holyoke in Latin. I must confess I was impressed with your delivery and, if I may say so, with your manner."

"Thank you, sir," said John, somewhat shyly.

"Well, you see, Mr. Adams, we need a good teacher for our little school in Worcester. It somehow occurred to me, when I saw and heard you, that you might fill the post with satisfaction."

"I hadn't thought of teaching," said John falteringly. He couldn't understand his own reluctance. Perhaps the memory of his dreary experience at Mr. Cleverly's school deterred him.

"Perhaps not," said Reverend Maccarty. "Indeed, on making inquiries, I understood you desired to enter the ministry. I thought you might want something in the meanwhile. And teaching in our school might even be a step toward it. I promise that you will be made comfortable."

John replied, after some hesitation, "I accept your offer. When do you want me?"

"Three weeks hence," said his visitor. "I will send a horse to fetch you on the appointed date. I am delighted that you can come."

True to his word, in three weeks Reverend Maccarty sent a messenger and horse to John. Setting out early in the morning, John made the whole journey of some sixty miles westward from Braintree in a single day.

True to his word, too, Reverend Maccarty had comfortable living quarters waiting for John at Mr. Green's. He was welcomed with good but simple food and an adequately furnished room.

The very next morning at eight John Adams entered the schoolhouse, a structure sixteen feet by twenty-four. He faced a roomful of squirming, fidgety, noisy youngsters, fifty perhaps in all, ranging in age from eight to fifteen. He promptly saw, as he had suspected, that he had a big job ahead of him, and he manfully set to his task.

A big job it certainly proved to be. Except for his own two younger brothers, John was not used to children. Lately he had been happy in the companionship of people his own age at Harvard, with whom he could exchange ideas and experiences. To teach children of such diverse ages called for the choosing of separate groups. To instruct them all at the same time, on different subjects, called for great concentration and patience.

At first the children seemed determined to make life a burden for the new teacher. John was equally determined to make them behave. He did not hesitate to punish the guilty by rapping them with a cane over the knuckles or on the palm of the hand. Being a just and an honest man, John never punished anyone until he was sure he deserved punishment. Because of John's fairness, he won the children's confidence and respect. Their behavior promptly improved. Being also a shrewd, intelligent man, he knew intelligence where he saw it; the intelligent and willing pupils benefitted by this, for he gave them the necessary instruction.

He brought back, after a hurried visit to Braintree, some cockleshells; he also encouraged the pupils to collect local stones. He used the shells and stones in teaching natural history.

He used the cane less and less, as the children saw he would stand no nonsense. As for John himself, he began to view his class as a sort of small community which he was called upon to govern wisely and well.

In this "little state," as he began to call it, he saw the world in miniature, a world peopled by "geniuses," "renowned generals but three feet high," and "politicians in petticoats."

"In sort, my little school, like the great world," he would say, "is made up of kings, politicians, divines, fops, fiddlers, sycophants, fools, coxcombs, chimney sweepers, and every other character drawn in history, or seen in the world."

It entertained him hugely to watch over this little world that was his school, and "to bestow the proper applause upon virtuous and generous actions, to blame and punish every vicious trick." He began to speculate as to which of his pupils would turn out in his maturity a hero, which a rake, which a philosopher, which a parasite . . .

It was a sort of game with John, this speculation, and it made life easier. But he was by no means content to remain in Worcester. Though the rolling hills, seen out of his window, were lovely, covered as they were with the green of oak, walnut, and chestnut trees; though the slopes were decked with pastures on which fine cattle grazed; though the valleys were rich in ash, birch, and maple, interlaced with colorful strips of wheat and flax, rye and Indian corn, his heart was in Braintree and in Boston.

There, by the sea, he had felt his imagination stirred. It was there that ships arrived from the world over, bringing alien cargoes and news of the great capitals. Seeing swarms of sails in the Boston harbor did something to quicken his mind and to arouse his curiosity as to how the other half of the world lived.

During 1755, John's first year in Worcester, he found himself stirred when the belated news arrived of the earthquake which destroyed the beautiful city of Lisbon, the capital of Portugal. Then, too, there was again a war between France and Great Britain. Actually war was declared the following year, but already it was waged in America in a very savage manner, resulting in the terrible butchery of General Braddock and his force of seven hundred men in the battle at Fort Duquesne.

Having moved from Mr. Green's to Doctor Nahum Willard's house, John Adams sat one evening discussing events with the doctor and his vivacious wife. Already John revealed political acumen and a prophetic sense.

"If we can only drive the troublesome French from this continent," said John Adams, his eyes alive and his voice vibrant, "there's no telling the greatness that awaits this country in the future. In the course of a century we English here may be more numerous than the English in England. As likely as not, with the growth of population and wealth, we shall build and maintain an immense navy which will command the seas and, if need be, subdue the united forces of Europe, should that continent be foolish enough to try and conquer us. Of course, I'm assuming that we'll unite to defend our shores. The only way to defeat us is to disunite us. *Divide et impera!*"

John's earnestness infected his listeners, who were astonished at the bold thought of the twenty-year-old speaker.

"In other words," said Dr. Willard, "you are suggesting that the time may come when this country will separate from England, and will achieve independence by a union of all the colonies?"

"Something like that," replied John, smiling. "I know what I said may sound wild, but history is full of such surprises."

"You've surely earned a cup of Bohea tea and a snack," said Mrs. Willard, laughing as she went off into the kitchen.

However homesick John may have been at the start in Worcester, he was being increasingly accepted by the community. As he saw more people he became more and more accustomed to his new life and surroundings. Worcester, indeed, was proud to have a teacher from Harvard for its school!

John had not yet decided whether he would enter upon a minister's career. But he was increasingly discouraged by the thought. This was because on all sides

he heard bitter theological disputes. Good Christians
though men might be, they differed on points of doc-
trine, and quarrels ensued which to John seemed futile.
His own beliefs, though deep, were simple. His forth-
right mind was attuned to fact and reason, and was
hostile to all quibbling and hairsplitting. He found
Reverend Maccarty reasonable and tolerant. John
would hate to disappoint him, as he would hate to disappoint his own father, by not entering the ministry.

One evening at a party at Judge Chandler's house
John met Mr. James Putnam, the Judge's son-in-law.
Though he had come to Worcester but six years before,
Mr. Putnam was already established as a lawyer and
respected and admired by the community.

An apt remark by John won Mr. Putnam's attention. The two became great friends. They went out
walking and shooting together, and John often visited
Mr. Putnam in the evenings.

It was a wonderful spring for John, yet he was troubled because he could take no part in the war. He
was too poor to have his own company, and had to
salvage his hurt pride by riding to Rhode Island whenever it was necessary to convey secret war documents.

At other times he would wander alone through the
fragrant woods of Worcester. He often sat on a stone
to rest and watch the woodpeckers as they extended
their long, fantastic tongues in search of the insects in
the bark of the trees. One day a small quail swooped
down, its breast shining creamy in the half shade. After
devouring a number of black ants near the tree trunks,
it disappeared into the undergrowth.

About the middle of May there was Court Week,

when dozens of lawyers and their servants in chaise or on horseback arrived in Worcester. Court Week was a time for festivity in the little town. Refreshment booths, horse racing, farmers' wrestling exhibitions, fiddle playing, and dancing kept the citizens in a gay whirl during the week.

It was the court sittings that interested John most. Since the school had a holiday during that week, every day John went to the court and listened with rapt attention to the cases, to the exchanges of argument between the opposing lawyers, and to the comments of the judges.

Each day John became increasingly fascinated. Young and impressionable, he tried to enter the minds of the lawyers, of the plaintiffs and defendants, and of the judges.

The precision of law, the hard sticking to facts, the logic used in the arguments, all appealed to him in a way that theology, with its differences and abstractions, never did.

Thinking the matter over at length, he decided to become a lawyer. It was a hard decision, because his father and many of his friends had counted on his becoming a minister. He could not do otherwise, however. For theology was alien to him, while law, he felt, he could understand.

He waited two or three months, however, before he took the first necessary step. In August of 1756, almost exactly a year after his arrival in Worcester, he signed a contract to study law with Mr. Putnam for two years.

Yet during these two years John often questioned himself. He had been dismayed by the disappointed attitude of his mother and father; even more by that of his own friends. Richard Cranch, whom he admired, wrote him that he was "inconsiderate, rash." Perhaps he should have remained in Braintree and been a farmer like Boylston and Elihu would be.

CHAPTER SEVEN

JOHN BECOMES A LAWYER

FTER THREE YEARS IN WORCESTER JOHN RETURNED
to Braintree, ready to take up his chosen voca-
tion of law. His father and mother, with heavy
hearts, had reconciled themselves to his decision.

"My son," said his father, who had aged consider-
ably, "I hope you have chosen wisely. I trust you will
not regret it. Whatever you do, you must do with
a full heart."

John, indeed, was keenly aware of his responsibility.
He must fail neither his father nor himself. He must
repay the sacrifices made on his behalf. His first duty
was to earn his own livelihood.

The difficulties he was facing suddenly seemed immense. John knew the law; he had studied hard. He
had read many books which few if any lawyers had

taken the trouble to read. Yet to open an office required money and patronage. He had neither.

Normally, his Worcester mentor, Mr. Putnam, would have stood sponsor for him. But John was utterly honest, and his irascibility had put him on bad terms with his teacher. He was too proud to seek help there If he had not been so honest, he might have obtained the position of Register of Deeds in Worcester. Then he could have gradually built up a practice there. But as a man of honor he felt it impossible to encroach on Mr. Putnam's field.

Moreover, ambition had begun to stir in young John. He resolved that he should not be just another lawyer. He determined to be a lawyer of distinction; he even aspired to be a greater lawyer than those of Greece and Rome or even modern England.

Back in Braintree the days seemed overlong. When not poring over legal books, John spent his time chatting, loading and unloading hay, sawing wood, or dining out with neighbors. It was good to smell the new-mown hay again and the fishy odors from the neighboring sea.

John wished for more and more law books which he found hard to obtain. He wanted to spend more time in Boston where he felt his future lay. But he was without financial resources.

His country friends begged him to undertake small local cases. Richard Cranch, with whom he spent many hours, was already a prosperous businessman. To be sure, he was nine years older than John. He had been born and educated in England, which gave a charming formality to his manners. But what John admired most was Cranch's extensive reading. They would sit for long hours and discuss famous books. When John left the Germantown house of Richard Cranch to ride home, he often felt he had learned as much as when he was studying with Mr. Putnam.

Delightful as such evenings were, they did not further him in his chosen profession. His family made him feel he was not doing his duty. One day his mother reproached him:

"You might have been a successful minister today if you had followed your father's wishes. At least, John, you might undertake some cases right here in Braintree and not spend all your time in Germantown."

John was hurt. In sheer desperation he undertook a small local case and lost it; he took another and lost that, too.

He began to wonder if, after all, he should not have gone into the ministry or continued digging ditches on the farm. He envied his brothers who were farmers and so much more contented than he was.

John began to ride to Boston more frequently. In the Boston court he met famous and influential lawyers. Finally he got up enough courage to ask them to help him. He was received coldly by one, but Mr. Gridley was more understanding of his predicament. He offered to present John to the court.

So in company with a neighbor, Edmund Quincy— old Colonel Josiah Quincy's son, and brother of John's Harvard friend, Samuel Quincy—John was sworn in, with his right hand on the open Bible. He stood motionless but inwardly shaking, as the Clerk of the Court intoned:

" 'You shall do no falsehood, nor consent to any being done in the court . . . You shall delay no man for lucre or malice, but you shall use yourself in the office of an attorney within the court according to the best of your learning and discretion and with all good fidelity as well to the court as to the client . . . "

Now the other lawyers came forward to shake his hand and that of Edmund Quincy. Then, according to custom, they all went together to Stone's Inn.

After his court presentation John spent even more time at the Quincy home. It was not Edmund, nor his brilliant younger brother, Josiah, who drew John there. It was the sister of these bright young men, the entrancing Hannah, whom many thought as witty and clever as any of her three brothers.

At this time Samuel, whom John had known well at college, was nearer Hannah than the others. Little did the devoted sister suspect that within fifteen years two of her brothers would be dead and Samuel would be fleeing with a thousand other Tories to England. This evening Hannah's loving eyes caressed young Samuel, but fifteen years later she was to write him, from her pain and bitterness, "Let it not be published that a brother of such brothers fled from his own country. Can you expect to walk uprightly now? Can you take fire in your bosom and not be burned?"

One night, just after John had left the Quincy home, young Hannah pirouetted lightly about the spacious parlor, her rose silk dress billowing like a balloon around her ankles.

"Listen to me, brothers mine," she laughed gaily. "I've snared the brainiest man in our part of the country. I can be Mrs. John Adams if I lift my little finger!" Hannah crooked her little finger as she extended her arm toward young Josiah, who was staring at her bright eyes and rosy cheeks as if he saw a witch.

"Why, Hannah!" exclaimed Edmund. "You made fun of John the other night. You laughed at him and all but called him a farmer's boy, not a lawyer. I saw how riled he was!"

"Mayhap it's a good thing for a young man to be riled," she saucily replied.

"John squires all the girls," Samuel said quietly, "but I doubt if he can marry any of them. He's far from rich, you know."

"But he will be some day," young Josiah insisted, his eyes shining, his face aglow with hero worship. "He'll be famous, too. Some day he will be richer and more famous than any of us Quincys!"

"Listen to him," teased Samuel. "You'd think he, not Hannah, was in love with John!"

"I don't care for slurs on the name of Quincy," Edmund frowned. He had glared at his young brother during his praise of John Adams.

"But, Edmund," Josiah defended himself, "you should hear how John talks to Jonathan Sewall! He can talk circles around your great Jonathan . . . that is, he sometimes does," Josiah amended, striving for strict honesty. "I know he always could if he really wanted to!"

Hannah, too, knew how much John enjoyed conversation with men; she couldn't pry him away. He seemed, at times, actually more interested in her brothers than in her. Hannah had often watched his eyes glancing about the room and picking upon whatever person he wanted to be with. He had strength and courage. He was so honest, Hannah knew, that no woman need fear the loss of his loyalty if he once set his heart on her. No, not even if she were made hideous by smallpox, a fate which had long frightened her as waves of the dread disease swept the Boston area.

The next afternoon when John arrived at the Quincy home Hannah was alone. The twilight was deepening, the shadows lengthening. Candles had not yet been lighted.

Hannah drew John to a seat beside her on the sofa. She chatted of Jonathan's engagement to her cousin Esther. How pleased the family was, how happy Esther was, how lucky Jonathan Sewall was!

John paid little heed to her words. It was enough to watch this lovely girl's animation, to listen to her excited, melodious voice.

Quite suddenly John felt that Hannah was everything that he desired. In the gathering darkness her face looked sweeter and more gracious than he had ever seen it.

As in a dream he heard himself saying, "Hannah, Hannah, I . . ."

"What are you two doing here in the dark? Where are the candles?" The door had burst open to admit a gay young woman and her escort, who John now realized was Jonathan Sewall.

John jumped to his feet.

"Why, cousin Esther," drawled Hannah, trying to cover her chagrin. "I hadn't expected you so early . . ."

As soon as Esther realized that she had interrupted them, she was embarrassed. She blushed and clung to Jonathan's arm, while John, who had time to recover some of his self-possession, congratulated his friend on his engagement and wished Esther great happiness.

Hannah had hurried from the room. Before she returned John took a hasty leave.

As he trotted his mare with unusual speed on the road home, he ruminated to himself on the subject of marriage. How many accidents govern the institution, John thought to himself. If Esther hadn't walked in at that exact moment, he might have committed himself to Hannah. His thoughts turned to Jonathan. He and Sewall had long been known to their friends as David and Jonathan because their intimacy recalled the Biblical heroes.

"Never were you more Jonathan to me than today," he spoke aloud in his thankfulness.

How easily his conversation with Hannah could have terminated in a courtship which would have terminated in a marriage. But he hadn't consolidated his position as a lawyer, yet, and until he did, he should not consider marriage.

When he reached Braintree he tethered his sweating horse in the barn. No home ever seemed friendlier than the barn that night.

He heaved sighs of relief as he stole quietly into his room. He flung himself into a chair and picked up Locke's *Essay on Human Understanding*, which he had been rereading. Books were far safer friends for an ardent young man than lovely maidens, he thought wryly.

This was a book you could read a hundred times and always find something new in it. John Locke based much of his reasoning on the behavior of animals and little children. John Adams could recall as clearly as John Locke himself when the talk of adults seemed mere gibberish to his young mind. He and Peter Boylston had invented their own words, which even now they sometimes used in fun.

In no time at all Hannah was just a memory, a memory more of an escape than of a lively nineteen-year-old girl. The number of his law cases was steadily increasing. These were heard in a room at the local meetinghouse reserved for this purpose, or occasionally at the home of Colonel Edmund Quincy, Hannah's Uncle Ned. Braintree had always been overrun with Quincys, but John had at last learned to chaff Hannah almost as successfully as she did him.

Even when his friend, Richard Cranch, became engaged, John stuck to his resolutions to give himself wholly to the law and to problems of the soil—planting and other farm matters which interested him fully as much as his present cases.

About this time the battle of Quebec was on every tongue, and girls' eyes brightened at the mention of General Wolfe as they darkened at the name of General Montcalm.

It was not long after the British victory that the bells tolled for the death of King George II, who had fallen on the palace floor. He was seventy-seven and now became to the Bostonians, "Our good old King!" How the bells did toll! Then they suddenly changed their tone and rang out with joy. Jubilantly they rang in Boston and Braintree and all up and down the Atlantic coast. "Long live King George III!" In 1760, with a young King on the throne, everyone in Boston and Braintree took heart. Surely good days were ahead!

The next spring, when John returned from attending court in Worcester, he found his mother awaiting him at the door. Her face was flushed. Her throat was wrapped in flannel. She was almost too hoarse to speak.

"Your father is very ill," she murmured. "You must go to him at once."

In riding boots and breeches, John raced up the stairs and into the sickroom. His father lay very still in the big four-poster. His labored breathing seemed oddly loud. John tiptoed to the bed and looked down at the unconscious old man. How old he looked! How worn and tired!

John just stood and stared, while his mother, who had followed him into the room, wept softly in a corner. Her tears distressed John as much as his father's difficult breathing. She had been quick to anger, quick to laugh, but he could never remember her crying. It was all so strange. It frightened him. It frightened Boylston and Elihu, too. The good doctor just shook his head. His face was very grave.

Within two days John's father was dead. For the next fortnight his mother was very ill. All the neighbors came to help. The women brought jelly and soup for his mother. The men helped John and his brothers with the farm chores. John felt as if a sturdy prop had fallen from beneath him; he felt empty and lightheaded.

It was Elihu, as merry and happy-go-lucky at twenty as he'd been at two, who took charge of their mother. John steadily felt that he could not stay here now; that he wanted a home of his own.

Richard Cranch came to see him and cheer him up; he suggested that John ride over to Parson Smith's with him one night and meet his fiancée. John listlessly consented, but kept putting Richard off.

He began to spend more time in Boston. He had discovered he had more than his share of human vanity.

He thirsted for fame and fortune. He was dissatisfied at the idea of a slow ascent to the top. He did all he could to spread his name; he talked and talked on every occasion.

John had, indeed, decided that popularity was, after virtue and wisdom, the most important thing to be achieved. He entered with extraordinary vigor into the fight against taverns. Such places, he said "become the eternal haunt of loose, disorderly people"; worst of all, in many towns "they were the nurseries of their legislators." In Braintree there were a dozen taverns, all filled every evening.

After vigorous campaigning, John succeeded in forcing a measure through a Braintree town meeting, limiting the taverns to three. His name was certainly becoming known locally!

In Boston, too, he had met his cousin, Samuel Adams, a man nine years his senior who was already deep in the politics of Boston. At his invitation John joined the famous Caucus Club, where "they smoked tobacco until you couldn't see from one end of the garret to the other."

At this time Samuel Adams was "a plump, round-faced, smooth-skinned, short-necked, eagle-eyed young politician," who spent his days and nights working against the Tories of England. The men who frequented his club were wardens or firewardens, assessors or collectors, with an occasional sprinkling of businessmen.

Mr. Gridley had honored John by inviting him with two other promising young lawyers to join the Sodalitas Club. Members met on Thursday nights to read together law treatises or such books as Tully's *Ora-*

tions or Rousseau's *Social Contract.* Points of law were debated with energy.

Gradually the pain of his father's death wore off. In October, 1761, John was finally sworn in before the Superior Court of Massachusetts. He dressed for this event in "gown and bands and tie-wig."

When he arrived home his mother asked, as she had so often of late, when he planned to marry. Relatives were always twitting him about being a selfish bachelor. " 'Who findeth a wife, findeth a good thing,' " one of the relatives quoted to him, and then suggested likely candidates for the position.

John was so irritated he hurried out of the house and resaddled his tired mare. He'd made up his mind he'd ride over to Germantown to Richard Cranch's. There was a sensible man, prosperous and kindly, a good friend. He realized that no man should marry too soon. Cranch was nearly ten years older than John and was only now marrying. Yes, it would do him good to see Cranch and philosophize until the early morning hours.

JOHN MARRIES ABIGAIL

B UT THERE WAS NO PHILOSOPHIZING THAT EVE-
ning. When John reached Germantown and
turned in at the gate of Richard Cranch's
large home, he encountered Cranch riding out.

"You've come at just the right time, Adams," he
greeted his young friend. "Now you shall have that
long-delayed introduction to the family of my future
wife. The Reverend William Smith will welcome any
friend of mine."

John turned his horse and rode along, half reluc-
tantly, half gladly. This was not at all what he had
counted on. Yet it might prove a good substitute. It
was said that Reverend Smith was a well-informed
man. John recalled that it was also said that Mrs.

71

Smith was an aristocrat who looked down on all Americans whose ancestors had not signed the famous Magna Charta in 1215, as hers had!

John smiled as he remembered this and the occasion when he was first told about it. One day young Abigail Smith, then a girl of fourteen or fifteen, was visiting the Quincys. Later John had told Hannah Quincy that she had an interesting young cousin. He further told her that he wished she would read the sort of books Abigail was reading. Hannah had laughed from the superior wisdom of her nineteen years. How foolish men were, especially men like John Adams! Nonetheless, Hannah had taken care to explain that Abigail's mother was overproud!

That was some years back. Since then he had often observed the serious young Abigail, who seemed shy among her elders but lively among her young friends. He knew her grandmother Quincy had educated her, that she had never gone to school. She looked frail during her early 'teens, but of late John had found her very attractive.

Perhaps, after all, this might prove an interesting evening.

While all these thoughts flitted through his head, he conversed with his friend Cranch, who was too full of his own affairs to pay much attention to John. This evening had been set apart to discuss Cranch's wedding plans.

As they entered the spacious parsonage, John wished he had taken better care of his personal appearance. Yet he could detect no difference in the greeting of the aristocratic Mrs. Smith.

"Any friend of Richard's is most welcome here," she graciously assured him.

John's bright eyes darted from one end of the large room to the other. There was Mary Smith, whom her friends and family called Polly, curtsying saucily, first to him, then to her fiancé. His eyes then lighted on a slight, slim-waisted figure, demurely attired in a brown wool dress with little white linen collars lying one upon the other, like a chain of beads around her throat. As he approached Abigail she rose and curtsied gracefully. All her movements were more controlled and graceful than any girl's he had ever seen.

Just as he was looking about for a chair near Abigail, the door to the parson's study opened. Reverend William Smith made an entrance, much as a king might make an entrance. John grinned to himself. As he later told Cranch on the return trip, the assembled company looked as if they were about to bow the knee to royalty!

Abigail's father nodded to his future son-in-law, then turned to John. "Come into my study with me, will you, Mr. Adams. There's a point I'd like to discuss with you."

He took John's arm and added, "We must leave the women to the wedding plans. There's no place for men in the parlor this evening."

For two hours John discussed every detail of farming with the parson, whose superior knowledge made him ill at ease. But John was never backward at repartee. He congratulated himself that on several occasions he made the amiable parson laugh most heartily.

By the time they rejoined the others, John felt he had made a good impression on Reverend Smith.

Young Abigail was sitting on the same, low stool, bending over the book she had been reading when John arrived. Her mother and handsome older sister were sitting somewhat apart, talking animatedly with Richard Cranch. John at once approached Abigail.

"What are you reading so assiduously?" he asked.

She turned the book so he might see the title, then raised her dark eyes shyly to his face, but said not a word.

"Why, it's John Locke's *Essay on Human Understanding!*" John was astonished. "Do you know it's one of my favorite books? I was rereading it quite recently."

Abigail blushed with pleasure.

"Do you usually read this sort of thing?" John asked, as he bent over her shoulder.

"I read everything I can find. Father lets me choose from his library. My Grandmother Quincy and Aunt Esther always let me choose at their homes, that is, since I'm older," she added softly.

"But I thought girls . . ."

John was interrupted by Mrs. Smith:

"I think you were about to observe, Mr. Adams, that the womanly virtues are confined to running the home efficiently and entertaining guests. My daughters are not deficient in any of these womanly arts, I can assure you. No, not even Elizabeth, who is not yet eleven!"

John bowed. What could he have done or said to offend Mrs. Smith? he wondered. There was no doubt that her voice was cool.

She was very distant when they took their farewells.

John couldn't say Mrs. Smith had been impressed favorably with him, but he was confident the parson liked him. Men usually did. And up to now he had managed to make himself pleasant to women.

He shrugged as he mounted his mare and trotted slowly home through the cool of the October night. Cranch turned off in Germantown, where the large round building which housed his glassworks loomed eerily in the starlit night. The village got its odd name because Cranch's partner had imported German glass workers.

How brightly the stars shone. Momentarily John wondered if he shouldn't have gone into the ministry after all. Then even the aristocratic Mrs. Smith would not have snubbed him!

Luckily he couldn't overhear the conversation which went on between the parson and his wife that evening after the young men left!

"I think our Abigail has a spark at last!" the parson had jovially observed to his wife, as soon as his daughters had retired.

"I presume you refer to young John Adams," she had replied with spirit. "The Adamses are no doubt worthy people, but *my* daughters . . ."

"Ah," her husband had countered softly, "your daughters, descendants of the Sieurs de Quincy, one of whom signed the Magna Charta. Where, hereabouts, can worthy suitors for such girls be found?" He swung his long arm in an arc which took in the countryside of Weymouth.

Mrs. Smith shrugged. As far as she was concerned the subject was closed.

As they were retiring for the night the parson took a

final fling at his wife's smugness: "Look at our little Abigail one day, see how pale and blank her dear face usually is, recall how few young men notice her . . ."

"She is but seventeen!" Mrs. Smith remarked, determined to have the last word.

All that winter John contrived to see Abigail whenever he possibly could, but rarely did they have a chance to talk in private. It was May, when the Braintree orchards were in full bloom and the air heavy with the perfume of the fruit blossoms, before these two found themselves momentarily alone. Abigail was visiting her Quincy grandparents, and John, not even aware of her presence, had arrived early. He had been bidden, as so often, to dinner there.

Abigail looked especially lovely on that May afternoon. There was a little color in her usually pale cheeks; her dark eyes were luminous. She wore a gray silk gown, simply made, but with a frill of lace around the neck.

"Shall we walk up the hill?" John suggested. "I like the view of Boston harbor in the late afternoon."

How graceful Abigail was, he thought, as they started out side by side.

"I've spent a third of my life here with Grandma Quincy," she said. "It's as much home to me as Weymouth. I know every path, almost every blade of grass."

"It must be wonderful to have your own grounds which go down to the seashore. I envy your grandfather."

Abigail smiled shyly. "It's odd to hear you say that, though I think many people do envy Grandpa.

I love to hear him talk with his friends. I always say I learn as much history that way as from my books."

"The sea has always fascinated me," John went on. "When I'm in Boston I haunt the harbor and docks if I can spare a minute from my law practice."

"Oh, do you?" Abigail's eyes shone with pleasure. "I would, too, but when I am with Aunt Elizabeth and Uncle Isaac I am not allowed to go out without a servant. I've wanted to go aboard one of the boats and sail away . . . far away."

"Away?" John looked at her with increased interest. "Where would you want to go?"

"Oh, to the East and the Spice Islands, to England to see the King! To France to meet the famous men there and to Italy to meet the men you so greatly admire! I've been rereading John Locke's *Essay on Human Understanding*. What a marvelous book it is!"

John was entranced. He could scarcely contain himself. To think he had found a young girl who not only had all the graces of a great lady, but who could exclaim with delight over the ideas of the British philosopher, John Locke!

He had long known he wanted to marry Abigail Smith and no one but Abigail Smith, yet he had postponed speaking to her father. He was still uncertain of her mother's attitude toward himself, although since Polly's marriage to Richard Cranch he was sure the older sister put in many good words for him at home.

All summer he saw Abigail as often as possible, but he still spoke only of books and mutual friends.

August was particularly sultry; September no better. John would return from Riding the Circuit, irritated and harassed. It was fatiguing to journey from place to place on horseback; sometimes he rode at night in order to reach a distant court session on time.

One day he vowed he would propose to Abigail before the week was out, but still he put it off. He had been invited to the Cranches for dinner. He knew he would see Abigail there, and he must speak before he saw her again.

So he started out early and rode to Weymouth. Before he reached the parsonage a terrific thunderstorm broke and he was caught in a torrent of rain. But he rode stubbornly on. He arrived, wet and disheveled, just as lightning struck a tree near the door.

Abigail, who had rushed downstairs when he pounded at the door, fell into his arms. She was trembling with fright.

John felt awkward and frightened. Scarcely knowing what he did, he bent and kissed her lips—just as her father opened his study door.

Disengaging herself, Abigail took John's hand, and together they followed Reverend Smith into his study.

"I had meant to speak first, sir," John stammered. "I love your daughter. I want to marry her. I shall never love any other woman."

"Sit down, young man," the parson said. "Dry yourself by my fire." He turned to his daughter, whose face was flushed. He thought he had never seen her look so handsome. He smiled fondly and said, "Go to your mother, Abby, and tell her the news."

Mrs. Smith was by no means as pleased with the engagement as her husband. She insisted Abigail was too young to think of marriage. Why, she was only eighteen! But if they would wait two years she would give her consent.

There was a gay celebration at the Cranches that evening. John was now Brother Adams, and Richard Brother Cranch!

John returned home in the late hours, more content than he had been in years. Much as he resented the two-year wait, he intended to use the time well. There would be a lifetime together, and he felt, humbly, that no lifetime was long enough.

About six months before the "probation" period was over, John made up his mind to be inoculated for smallpox. He wanted Abby to be inoculated, too; but her mother was horrified and flatly refused to consider what she termed "such modern nonsense." So John went to Boston that April for a six weeks' quarantine. The Quincy brothers, Samuel and Josiah, were fellow patients. John had no fear. Hadn't his own mother's uncle, Dr. Zabdiel Boylston, introduced the practice into Boston?

He and Abby kept up a spirited correspondence during the weeks of separation. He "dreamed he saw a Lady tripping over the hills on the Weymouth shore and spreading light and beauty and glory all around her." As for Abby, her concern was for his health: "They" [the doctors], she wrote, "are all agreed that 'tis best to abstain from Butter and Salt—the most of them from meat."

"Keep your spirits up," she admonished him. Or she wrote tenderly: "Mamma is so fearful I should catch the distemper that she hardly ever thinks the letters are sufficiently purified. Did you never rob a bird's nest? Do you remember how the poor bird would fly round and round, fearful to come nigh, yet not know how to leave the place? So they say I hover 'round Tom while he is smoking your letters."

Meanwhile John's head ached. He burned with fever and broke out into pustules. But he soon recovered and could go home.

All that last summer after John returned he spent as much time as possible getting his little house and garden, which he had inherited from his father, ready for his bride. It was a small house, but it had been built to endure through the years. The walls of brick and clay were sheathed in sturdy wood, already fifty years old, and weathered to a grayish brown. It stood close to his mother's house and was similar in size and shape. Both houses faced the Old Shore Road, beyond which rose the green slopes of Penn's Hill, where John, as a little boy of ten, had watched for the French fleet. It had long been home to John Adams; now it would be home in quite another fashion.

Little by little it was being filled with Abigail's belongings. A load of linens or blankets, the contents of her modest trousseau, was brought over from time to time and stored in the proper places. It was growing bit by bit, under his happy eyes, from "my" home into "our" home.

Yet the days seemed long, overlong, before the 25th of October arrived. The wedding day dawned clear and cold. The festivities were such as John could scarcely bear. He had no idea so many people could crowd into the parsonage, which had been decorated with flowers and fruit for the occasion.

At last the sacred words had been said.

At last, too, Abigail could run away from the gay throng, wrapped in her green woolen cloak and hood. John leapt from the waiting carriage to assist her.

Together young Mr. and Mrs. John Adams drove off from the Weymouth parsonage and the chatting relatives and friends, into the cool calm of the October afternoon.

John's heart beat so he could hardly breathe. He was at last bringing his bride home.

He looked tenderly at the shy girl at his side. God grant he would be able to make her proud of him, he prayed.

CHAPTER NINE

THE LIBERTY TREE

J OHN WAS TROUBLED. BRAINTREE WAS IRRITATED. Boston was angry. The cause of all this trouble, irritation, and anger was the Stamp Act, a measure which the British Parliament had passed without consulting the American colonies.

George Grenville, Prime Minister of England who had proposed this manner of raising money to defray the expenses of constant wars, had thought it would meet with the approval of the Americans. Never was a well-meaning man more mistaken. Even the ill and aged William Pitt came from his sickbed to the House of Commons in London to speak against the Stamp Act.

82

A less famous member, a tyro in fact, named Edmund Burke, also spoke in favor of the colonial position, but his opinions were scarcely noted.

However, Grenville's ministry fell, and the young Marquis of Rockingham took his place at the helm. Rockingham was a man of excellent sense who held liberal opinions. He agreed with William Pitt that not only Americans but eight million of the nine million Englishmen who were without the vote in England should have a right to express their opinions. It seemed to these Englishmen a matter for home reform as well as colonial reform.

Meanwhile John was painfully aware that the men of Braintree were in an increasingly bellicose mood. He could not walk a block from his Boston law office without hearing threats to run the Crown Officers through—"so thoroughly that you'd be able to see daylight," men would add with a bitter laugh. Crowds gathered around various taverns and on every street corner.

It was a sultry summer. Abigail's first child was born the middle of July and was named for her mother. Abigail's father came over from Weymouth to christen the baby.

John was often obliged to be away from home on law business. He disliked leaving his wife and baby alone when the country was in such a vengeful mood. He dreaded mobs.

Finally he decided to remain at home for a fortnight or more to help with the haying and other farm chores. Sometimes he would ride off to the pits for gravel; another day he would repair the fences. Working on the farm still gave him a sense of well-being.

In the evenings, after admiring tiny Abby, he would sit with his young wife, feeling safe and at rest. He had at last finished writing "Dissertation on the Canon and Feudal Law." The trials of the Pilgrims, and the hardships faced by his less remote ancestors, were often in his thoughts. From time to time he read to Abigail bits he had written, and warmed with pride when he saw the approval on her face and the admiration in her eyes.

" 'Let us read and recollect and impress upon our souls the views and ends of our more immediate forefathers, in exchanging their native country for a dreary, inhospitable wilderness. Let us examine into the nature of that power and the cruelty of that oppression which drove them from their homes. Recollect their amazing fortitude, their bitter suffering, the hunger, the nakedness, the cold, which they patiently endured, the severe labors of clearing their grounds, of building their houses, raising their provisions amid dangers from wild beasts and savage men, before they had time or money or materials for commerce . . .' "

"That is splendid, John," Abigail said when her husband momentarily ceased reading.

" 'Let us recollect it was liberty,' " John continued reading, " 'the hope of liberty, for themselves and us and ours, which conquered all discouragements, dangers and trials . . .' "

The baby began to cry. Abigail picked her up and gently rocked back and forth to quiet her.

"I remember the other day, John, that you said America was not a new country but the heir of Greece and Rome and of the laws of England." Abigail spoke softly, looking over her baby's shoulder. "It's true,

John! I've heard my father and his friends say the same."

"Yes, we are heirs of the laws of England, but this Stamp Act is pure folly!" John rose from his chair and paced up and down, his face becoming quite red. "It is designed to strip us from the means of knowledge by loading the press and the colleges with endless restraints and duties. It is a scandalous thing to strip the poor and fill the pockets of collectors and their deputies. Why, it is positively feudal in its implications!"

Abigail was surprised to see her husband so upset, and still more astonished to hear him express opinions which she had heard expressed by his cousin, Samuel Adams, one evening last spring, when she met the older man for the first time.

John was thinking that something new had come into his life ever since he had heard, some four years ago, fiery James Otis inveigh against the Molasses Act and the Writs of Assistance. It had certainly inspired John to undertake this, his first considerable literary effort. If only his essay could help the cause!

He took "The Dissertation on the Canon and Feudal Law" to James Otis in Boston about the beginning of August.

"I don't know if you'll like it, sir," John said shyly. "It isn't such a wonderful bit of prose, but it is timely, I think."

"If it's as strong as your letters in the *Gazette* on the government, your cousin Sam will be delighted to see it in print," Mr. Otis observed, as he leaned back in his chair to read.

John waited impatiently; it seemed more like hours than minutes to him. From time to time James Otis would grunt. Was it from satisfaction? John asked himself.

Suddenly Otis flung the papers down on his work table and jumped to his feet. He seized John's hand and shook it warmly.

"This is something like it!" James Otis grinned with delight. "It's just what we need! I hadn't a notion that I would read such sentiments from your pen, Adams!" Otis reached for his coat which he had removed in the heat.

"Come with me, young man, and I'll introduce you to Edes and Gill. You can see where the *Gazette* is printed. Mayhap you'll pause on Queen Street long enough to help set the type."

When the first section was in print it took up two of the paper's four pages. John proudly presented a copy to Abigail.

"I wish you could have signed it," she said, her eyes shining. "It's wonderful, John."

"It will take some four issues to print all of it and by then my identity will be discovered, I imagine." John looked troubled rather than pleased.

"How is it in Boston?" asked Abigail, as she took the baby from her cradle to show to John. "Isn't she sweet?"

"She's sweet, but Boston's sour, Abigail. Mr. Otis told me that he had seen three fights. Ugly-looking customers are gathering on all the street corners. I heard that householders are barring their windows and barricading their doors."

Abigail frowned. "I'm glad you're safe out here in Braintree," she said, looking at the tiny bundle in her arms.

At the junction of Essex and Newbury Streets in Boston stood a tremendous elm tree known as "the great tree." Hanging to a limb of this tree, one hot morning in the middle of August, were found two effigies such as the people of Boston usually made for Guy Fawkes Day and other riotous holidays. But this day the effigies were not hanging there for fun. There was no gaiety about the passing people who glanced furtively at the huge jackboot, from which stuck a head with horns, like the devil himself.

The startled people whispered, guessing all too accurately that this was meant to represent Lord Bute, who, over in England, intended to force the Stamp Act on the unwilling colonies. The other effigy was most certainly Mr. Andrew Oliver. Wasn't it labeled "Stamp Officer," so that no one should make a mistake? Mr. Oliver, the local deputy, was the brother-in-law of Lieutenant-governor Thomas Hutchinson, and he would have the business of overseeing the hated Stamp Act in Massachusetts.

All day the people passed by the tree. All day those effigies remained hanging from the great elm, undisturbed. When John rode back to Braintree they were still there.

He said nothing to Abigail, but she had heard about the figures from others. Everyone was talking of liberty. The following night, when he returned home, Abigail walked out to meet him.

"What is the news in Boston today, John?" she asked eagerly.

John shook his head as he slipped from his tired horse. Bridle over one arm, the other around his wife, he walked slowly into his yard toward the barn.

"At dusk last night they took the effigies down and placed them on a bier," he told her. "A crowd collected, no one knows just how, but forty or fifty persons sur-

rounded the elm tree by dark. They began to shout:
'Liberty and property! No stamps!' Almost as if it were
a signal, Abby," he went on, "more people appeared.
They surged down King Street to Oliver's dock, where
he had built that small office believed to be the Stamp
Office. In five minutes they had destroyed it. Placing
the effigies on top of the wreckage, they set fire to it.
Then like crazy people, cheering and shouting, they
turned and started toward Fort Hill, stopping on the
way at Mr. Oliver's house. They swarmed through his
house, broke his windows and smashed his furniture,
while his frightened family hid upstairs . . ."

"Oh, no!" gasped Abigail, turning her eyes toward
her own small house, so snug and safe here in the
country, protecting her tiny baby.

"I tell you, Abby, I don't like mobs," John resumed,
as they turned from the barn back toward the house.

"I'm terrified of them," she agreed.

"They destroyed his fence and tore up the garden,
just senselessly destroying everything they could find.
This is not the way to show our anger. This is not the
way to impress the British Parliament," said John with
conviction.

"Do you think your cousin Sam . . ."

John shook his head. "I don't know, Abby, I just
don't know. He wouldn't admit it if he had." John
paused. "More likely the people of Boston heard of
Virginia's resolutions and were inspired by their courage and Patrick Henry's eloquence and firmness to resist."

The following day John had to leave for Martha's
Vineyard to attend to important legal business. He

was extremely uncomfortable about leaving his wife and gave many instructions to his mother and brothers as to her comfort and safety.

That day Governor Bernard issued a proclamation offering one hundred pounds reward for the conviction of those concerned in the riot.

On the very day of this proclamation another crowd assembled and marched again to Mr. Oliver's house. This was too much for Mr. Oliver. He announced that he would resign his office and never act in the capacity of Stamp Collector. His promise delighted the mob, who proceeded to Fort Hill and built a bonfire in honor of the victory.

The crowd danced jubilantly around the bonfire. Soon they found this rather dull and decided they should march to the home of Lieutenant-governor Hutchinson.

They shouted to him to come out onto his balcony and proclaim publicly that he did not favor the Stamp Act. When there was no response it was decided that he had gone to his country place. So they threw stones and smashed all his windows before they dispersed.

By this time everyone in Boston was talking of "The Liberty Tree." Young and old, rich and poor, even little children, walked by it daily.

Toward the end of August a bonfire was started on King Street not far from the scene of John Adams' boyhood adventures with the press gangs. A boisterous mob soon gathered. Before long they attacked the house opposite the north side of the Courthouse. Here the public files were kept, and books of accounts. These were promptly destroyed. The fires grew larger, the flames sprang higher, the mob became hilarious and stubborn. They looked about for further fields to conquer.

Their eyes turned to the new and elegant home of the Controller of Customs. They tore down the fences, broke the windows, and entered. Inside they broke the fine furniture, imported china and glassware, anything on which they could lay their hands. Then they drank up the contents of the wine cellar and became more furious and barbarous than they had been before.

When they finally reached Thomas Hutchinson's home they were wholly out of hand. Here they destroyed or carried away or cast into the street the entire contents, demolished everything except the brick walls, and when daylight overtook them they were at work breaking through these. The Royal Governor only learned of the disturbance when it was over. He at once summoned the Council.

The Bostonians themselves assembled in Faneuil Hall, that famous narrow building with its tiers of long, curved windows one above the other, with its steep, sloping roof from which tiny dormers peeked out on each side of the sturdy belfry. Unanimously they voted against such violent mob proceedings.

Hadn't poor Mr. Hutchinson walked down the aisle of the Superior Court in his shirt sleeves, tears streaming down his face? He begged the Court to overlook his strange appearance, as he had no other apparel; nor had his family fared any better. He turned to the assembled crowds and spoke in a broken voice:

"I call God to witness that I never in New England

or Old, in Britain or America, aided or supported what is commonly called the Stamp Act, but did all in my power to prevent it . . . I hope all will see how easily the people may be deluded, inflamed, carried away with madness against an innocent man . . . I pray God give them better hearts."

When the news of these happenings spread through Massachusetts, John was at Martha's Vineyard, trying one of his most difficult cases.

As he rode home through the bright September days, he thought mostly of Abigail and little Abby. He had given his brothers many directions as to their protection if mobs should riot. But good and kind as Elihu and Peter Boylston were, John knew it was his duty to protect his own wife and child.

He knew, too, that Braintree must soon take a stand on one side or the other. The Stamp Act would show where a man stood. His village was small; only some fifteen hundred persons lived there. But it must none-theless take its stand.

Soon after John reached home he drew up "Instructions of the Town of Braintree to their Representatives." He had given long and careful thought to these matters. His conclusion rang out as clearly as ever James Otis' or his cousin Sam's had:

" 'We further recommend the most clear and explicit assertion and vindication of our rights and liberties to be entered on the public records, that the world may know, in the present and all future generations, that we have a clear knowledge and just sense of them, and, with submission to Divine Providence, can never be slaves.' "

Printed in the Boston *Gazette* it rang through Massachusetts and was adopted by no less than forty other towns as their instructions to their own representatives.

Abigail glowed with pride. Her happiness would have been complete had her husband not been so often away from home. In order to support his family John had to Ride the Circuit, to follow the court from town to town, often far from Braintree.

When October 31 dawned clear and bright, everyone spoke of it as the last day of liberty.

On November 1 the Stamp Act became law.

The bells began to toll at dawn. Beginning at the South Meeting House, the clang of bells were echoed from steeple to steeple. Down the Atlantic coast from Maine to the Carolinas the bells tolled.

In New York they held a funeral procession. The guns boomed to announce the death of liberty. Ships in the harbor lowered their flags.

On the famous Liberty Tree in Boston swung the effigy of Grenville. Toward evening a crowd gathered, a crowd no longer boisterous. The effigy was removed and carried to the gallows in the Neck, where they hanged it.

The quiet which came over the country was more ominous than the rioting. It was said that the hated Stamp Act had done more to unite the colonies than any prior act or law passed by the Parliament in faraway England.

CHAPTER TEN

THE BOSTON MASSACRE

THE NEXT SPRING FOUND JOHN WORKING HARD ON his farm. The courts had been closed because of the opposition to the Stamp Act; during the winter his law business had been nonexistent.

John had worked up a prosperous law business. He had even been able to buy a sulky to drive from court to court. It was especially discouraging, after two years of such hard work, to have the courts closed. Even marriages could not take place. Everything was at a standstill.

He had tried in vain to hide his concern from his young wife. There was nothing to do but make the

94

best of the difficult situation. Fortunately there was one bright side to it: despite his straitened circumstances, he could spend more time in his little home.

A new tranquillity came to John as he drove his cattle through the snowdrifts that spring, then hurried to his warm home. It gave him some diversion to drive Abigail from time to time to tea at Colonel Quincy's, where the talk was usually of resistance and liberty.

One balmy spring evening John turned from his law books and suggested that they reread *The Merchant of Venice.*

"Remember, Portia," he said, putting his arm around Abigail's waist, "when we read this play on Penn's Hill overlooking the bay?"

Abigail drew her chair nearer to her husband's and took her mending from the bag which hung on the chair arm. As she quietly sewed, John's clipped English flowed out in the magic words of Shakespeare:

> " 'The quality of mercy is not strain'd,
>   It droppeth as the gentle rain from heaven
>   Upon the place beneath: it is twice blest,
>   It blesseth him that gives, and him that
>   takes . . .' "

John raised his eyes and saw the admiring look in Abigail's eyes. "Whatever would I do without my Portia?" he asked.

When he finished reading, Abigail went into the kitchen, returning presently with teapot and cups. They drank Bohea tea in happy silence until she asked:

"Didn't I see you reading *King Henry VIII* the other day, dearest?"

John's eyes lighted up. "Indeed you did! I found just the passage I wanted and memorized it."

He jumped to his feet and stood before her, his plump, short form drawn up to its greatest height. His hands under his coattails, he walked back and forth as he declaimed:

" '. . . for, upon these taxations,
The clothiers all, not able to maintain
The many to them 'longing, have put off
The spinsters, carders, fullers, weavers, who,
Unfit for other life, compell'd by hunger
And lack of other means, in desperate manner
Daring the event to the teeth, are all in uproar,
And danger serves among them.' "

"I recited this the other night to the Sons of Liberty, and it went very well."

Abigail smiled. "Your cousin Sam has made you quite at home with the braisiers, painters, and jewelers of Boston, hasn't he?"

"As for you, my dearest Diana," John retorted gallantly, "you have made me feel at home with the rich Boston merchants."

"Methinks, dearest," Abigail teased him, "you really prefer dining at Nick Boylston's elegant table to Cousin Sam's!"

John laughed shortly. "My Cousin Sam dines on liberty," he said. "It's heady victuals for a farmer, but you know, Abby, I'm growing fond of the fare."

The news of the repeal of the Stamp Act reached Boston that week. John was busy with local politics and could not get to Boston for the great celebration.

He heard from friends of the pyramid of two-hundred and eighty lanterns that the Sons of Liberty had erected on the Boston Common. Everyone said it was the greatest celebration since the fall of Quebec. The fireworks of beehives, wheels, and serpents were vividly described for weeks. Every house in Boston had been lighted; from cellar to attic the candles flickered.

In John Hancock's big stone house facing Boston Common, the Sons of Liberty had dined together. John knew it had been a proud day for his cousin Sam when he won Hancock, the richest man in Boston, to their cause.

Even though he missed the celebration John felt he had much for which to be thankful. The courts were reopening, business was resuming its normal course, and the ships in the harbor were beginning to unload their cargoes.

When summer came Abigail presented her husband with a son. They named him John Quincy, after Abigail's grandfather, Colonel Quincy of Wollaston Hill.

The ten mile ride to and from Boston seemed longer than ever to John. He began to consider moving into town. His mother had remarried; his brothers were settled with their own families near her. So when the next summer came, he rented a three-story brick house painted white, with a little garden in the rear. It was on Brattle Street, in the center of Boston. He had his law office downstairs with a separate entrance. The Townhouse, where the Legislature now met, was only two blocks away.

Almost from the first day his law business increased miraculously. Abigail and Cousin Sam had been right, John decided, when they urged him to move to Boston. He had never felt so cheerful and so well. He often looked down King Street and remembered his fright the time he hid from the impressment gang.

Well, perhaps England would learn that she was dealing with fellow Englishmen, he often mused as he jounced laughing baby John on his knee or watched little Abby trot around in her starched white skirts. She adored her father, whom she resembled, and would rush to him as soon as she heard his voice. Then she would laugh aloud when he threw her into the air and caught her again in his outstretched arms.

One evening John's old friend, Jonathan Sewall, came to call and invited himself to dinner. John was amused as he watched Sewall treating Abigail with Tory gallantry. Jonathan was now Attorney General.

Later that evening, when Abigail had retired and the two friends were smoking their long-stemmed pipes, he turned to John and said:

"I was asked by Governor Bernard to offer you the vacant office of Advocate General in the Court of the Admiralty."

He put his hand lightly on John's knee as he bent nearer him. "Don't refuse it, old friend, without consideration," Jonathan begged. "It's a lucrative office, as you know, and a good step up the ladder to fame and fortune."

John Adams puffed quietly at his pipe. "I can't consider it, Jonathan," he said firmly.

"But you've taken no part in politics since you moved to Boston," Jonathan expostulated. "It's unfair to your handsome young wife and your children to refuse it."

"Nevertheless I must," John spoke more firmly than before. "I cannot do otherwise, Jonathan."

When Sewall finally left, John knew they had come to the parting of the ways. These were times when men must take sides. John Adams had chosen his.

John now had two clerks in his law office. He had been able to give Abigail a maid, as well as a boy to clean shoes and doors and generally help out Sukey, the faithful Negro girl who had come with them from Braintree.

That September, ships-of-war from the British fleet at Halifax came up and anchored off Boston, extending from North Battery to south of the Long Wharf. Their cannons were loaded, with tampions out, as if they expected a long siege. Here, John told Abigail, were the "teeth" he had warned were hidden in the Townshend Acts, which the Bostonians had overlooked in their excitement over the Stamp Act. Here were four thousand soldiers in bright red coats to remind the people that King George III still ruled.

Soon the shops and the markets swarmed with redcoats, "lobsters" the angry people called them. The British officers got the best of everything, leaving only the inferior fish and meat for the Bostonians.

"It's intolerable!" John shouted at Abigail one dark November night when he came home, in a rage because, as often happened, a sentinel had challenged him at his very door. "I shall have trouble, Abby! I almost assaulted a sentry." John paused, then added quietly, "I half wish I had!"

Abigail said nothing. She was used to her husband's temper and knew that his rage left as suddenly as it came.

"We shall be forced to move," John went on. "I can't stand sentries at my very doorstep."

"I'd be glad to be away from the sound of the perpetual fife and drum, the constant marching feet," Abigail agreed. "It isn't good for the children to look out of their windows and see men being whipped on their bare backs, to hear the screams of pain, or see a man shot, which we saw the other day."

"Perhaps we should go back to Braintree . . ."

Memory of his old home flooded John. Still, calm, serene, cool, peaceful . . . Out of one window there he could see Mount Wollaston, and beyond that Stony Field Hill, covered with corn and fruits; out of the other window an orchard, and beyond that the long marsh they called the broad meadow. From the east window of the opposite room he could see a fine plain covered with corn, and beyond that the whole harbor and all the islands. From the end window of the same room, if he used a prospect glass, he could see every ship, sloop, schooner, or brigantine that went in and out.

"Braintree," he repeated. "There was never a finer spot than ours in Braintree."

"There's so little room there," Abby protested. "If we can some day buy the other house from your brother, Peter Boylston, and put them together, it would make a pleasant summer home. But for now, John, your business is here in Boston. We can find another rent farther from the soldiers, I am sure."

Another daughter, named Susanna for John's mother, was born the next December. She was a frail, sickly child from birth. Dr. Joseph Warren, John's friend from the Sons of Liberty, couldn't find any way to make the baby stronger. Abigail and John worried and worried about the little child, but she didn't improve.

The next fall John moved his family to a large house in Cold Lane.

It was a particularly severe winter. In February the harbor froze. John's legal business kept him from home a great deal, and his free time was spent in the office of the *Gazette* or with the Sons of Liberty. He saw less of Abigail than when she was in Braintree, he often complained. He disliked leaving her alone at night, as he sometimes had to do. Abigail had become very nervous, for the soldiers grew more and more violent and the people of Boston more sullen. Even in Cold Lane the redcoats seemed to be everywhere.

John was feeling unusually discouraged one night as he rode slowly down Hanover Street and turned into Cold Lane. He left his horse at the livery stable and walked home. Inevitably a sentry challenged him. John answered the redcoat more curtly than usual. Again he felt like knocking the fellow down. It was insufferable to be treated like a prisoner.

He went to bed that night determined to return to Braintree. An hour after he was in bed he was awakened by the sound of serenading. Men's deep voices rose above the music of violins and flutes.

"The Sons of Liberty are serenading you, John!" Abigail exclaimed. "They have been here before, when you were away."

John went to the window in his nightshirt and leaned out. Torches flared and the song reached his ears more clearly:

"John Adams, we sing to you . . ."

His name! Could it be? He turned back into his room and dressed as fast as possible. Then he ran down to admit the singers into the house. There were some dozen of them, mechanics and artisans and Mr. Edes the printer. He knew only three or four of them by name.

They told John they had missed him, that they feared for Boston with the redcoats about, that they hadn't meant to disturb him but just wanted to let him know they needed him and were his friends.

When they left and John returned to their bedroom, Abigail could see he had been deeply touched.

On the evening of March 5, 1770, John Adams went to his club in South Boston to attend a regular meeting. About nine o'clock he and his friends were alarmed by the ringing of bells.

Was it a fire?

They ran out into the street and learned that the British soldiers and the Boston mob had come to serious blows.

John's first thought was for Abigail. Little Susanna had died only a short time before and Abigail was alone in the house with the other children. He set off at once for home. The streets were fairly deserted, but he ran into a crowd of people near King Street. They were surging toward the Custom House, where they grabbed a sentinel.

"Here's the man who struck the barber's boy!" someone shouted.

The sentinel backed away, shoved the rammer down his musket and primed it. Chunks of wood and sharp-edged pieces of ice were pelted at him from all sides. Nasty epithets accompanied the missiles. Suddenly the sentinel dodged away and ran for his life.

For months past John Adams had feared an explosion. As he tried to circle the crowd, he caught sight of Captain Preston, attended by eight redcoats. They appeared to be going to the aid of the sentinel.

The crowd was shouting madly:

"Lobsters! You're afraid to fire!"

"Lobsters! Let's burn the sentry box!"

"Come on, boys!"

One of the soldiers lost his footing when a missile struck him violently.

No one heard the order to fire.

John was by then a long distance from the scene of the trouble. He had run most of the way and his lantern was out. He thought he heard shots ring out just as he reached home.

He rushed inside and found the little family gathered together, both children screaming.

He took little Abby in his arms and tried to quiet her.

"Now, now, my darling," he soothed her. "Your father's here, it's all right. Nothing shall harm you, sweetheart."

"I'm so glad you're home, John," Abigail said fervently, as she tried to quiet young John Quincy who had taken up his sister's screams. "Didn't I hear shots?"

"I thought I heard some, Abby. Probably they fired over the heads of the crowd to disperse them. I hate mobs, Abby."

"I don't like it," Abigail said suddenly. "I feel afraid. There go those alarm bells again, louder and louder. Something frightful may have happened."

"Yes, Abby," John agreed soberly. "I came through a line of drawn-up redcoats."

He saw his wife's distress was increasing.

"But now we must get the children back to bed," he said firmly. "See, little Abby is already asleep in my arms."

Abigail took John Quincy by the hand. He had grown quiet and was rubbing his sleepy eyes.

"We should go to bed ourselves and try to sleep," John said.

"Yes, that is the only sensible thing," Abigail agreed as they mounted the stairs to the chambers above.

But neither John nor Abigail slept that night.

CHAPTER ELEVEN

JOHN'S GREAT COURAGE

THE NEXT MORNING, AS JOHN MADE HIS WAY TO his office near the State House, he found the streets overrun with people, grim country people for the most part. They all carried muskets, many with their clothes tied ridiculously to the gun barrels —of all places! thought John sourly. This must be some of Cousin Sam's brewing, he decided. Just then he recognized Ben Edes, printer of the *Gazette*.

"Good morning," he greeted Edes. "Were many killed last night?"

"Four," Ben replied. "One was Sam Gray, the ropewalker who started the fight on the docks a few nights ago. Another was a big mulatto you must have seen often . . ."

John nodded.

"The other two were just harmless spectators. There they stood, looking on; there they were slaughtered. One a sailor and the other a lad of only seventeen . . . Dr. Warren's with him—the boy's in agony and is dying slowly. Captain Preston's in jail. He ought to be hung and so ought all the other redcoats!" Ben Edes spat with vigor, narrowly missing John's polished boot.

Again John nodded. Then he said roughly, "Better get those country men back home. Must be thousands of them in Boston this morning. Better put a watch on. There's likely to be more trouble tonight."

John turned into his office, his face and attitude so dour it made Ben think of a thundercloud.

Captain Preston in prison! repeated John to himself as he sat down at his desk. His hatred of mobs rose so violently within him that he was almost overcome with nausea. This must stop! There would be more bloodshed, there would be more rioting, unless the crowds were promptly dispersed and sent back to the country where they belonged.

John glanced idly at a book on his desk. It was a new acquisition from London, the recently translated *On Crimes and Punishments* by a famous Italian, the Marchese de Beccaria. Surprised by the appropriateness of the title, he opened it and turned the pages idly. Suddenly his glance lighted on a passage which he paused to read:

"If, by supporting the rights of mankind and of invincible truth, I shall contribute to save from the agonies of death one unfortunate victim of tyranny or of ignorance equally fatal, his blessing and tears of transport will be a sufficient consolation to me for the contempt of all mankind."

John was carried away by this passage. Just as he started to reread the courageous words, he heard a violent knocking on his office door.

A man called Forrester, known to everyone in Boston as "the Irish infant," burst into his office. John was startled to see tears streaming from his eyes. His clothes were disheveled; he was gasping for breath.

"Sit down, Mr. Forrester," suggested John quietly, trying to restrain his astonishment. "What can I do for you?"

"Captain Preston is innocent! I swear on my honor he is innocent!" his visitor shouted between deep breaths, gesturing wildly. "You must help him. He is going to be murdered if you don't help him! I've been everywhere. No lawyer will undertake his defense."

"So last of all you come to me," observed John wryly.

"I had to come to you. There was nowhere else to go. You are known to be against the soldiers, but someone must defend them." Mr. Forrester paused for breath, then continued passionately: "You must defend Captain Preston. He's in jail, with his eyes swollen shut. He's been questioned all night long. He is desperate. We are all desperate. No one has slept . . ."

John nodded. He and Abigail had lain awake, too.

"You must come to his aid," repeated the overwrought "Irish infant." "I've seen Mr. Auchmuty, the Admiralty Judge. Mr. Auchmuty said he'd act for Captain Preston on this one condition—that you would serve with him."

As John made no reply, Forrester rushed on, "I've

been next door to see young Josiah Quincy, Jr. He made the same answer. He'll serve only if you do. Have pity on the poor soldiers—eight of them are in jail, too, also awaiting trial for murder. Have pity . . . Help them . . ." he begged, putting his hand across the desk toward John's tightly closed fist.

Even as he sat here facing Forrester, Sam Adams and the Sons of Liberty were probably stirring up the boiling cauldron of hatred and unrest, hoping it would overflow.

What a fool Sam was, thought John sourly. He'd never defeat powerful England with untrained mobs. Unruly mobs could only lead to further bloodshed and more repressive reprisals. Liberty! What was liberty? Surely not liberty for mobs to hang men whose guilt had not yet been proven!

John opened again the Marchese de Beccaria's book. His eyes sought the passage he had recently read. He read again:

"If, by supporting the rights of mankind and of invincible truth, I shall contribute to save from the agonies of death one unfortunate victim of tyranny or of ignorance equally fatal, his blessing and tears of transport will be a sufficient consolation to me for the contempt of all mankind . . ."

John heard, as if from a great distance, Forrester repeating over and over again: "Captain Preston is innocent! He is innocent! He is innocent!"

Tears were again streaming down Forrester's face.

"Before Almighty God, I swear the man is innocent!" His voice rose hysterically. "Captain Preston acted in self-defense!"

John raised his hand.

"That will be decided at his trial," said John firmly. "I cannot promise to defend Captain Preston and the soldiers until I have first investigated the matter and ascertained their innocence. I will look into the evidence. If I find that Captain Preston acted in self-defense and that he cannot have a fair trial without my assistance, I will defend him. I promise that!"

"You'll defend him!" Forrester repeated exultantly.

"I will gather the evidence," said John quietly. "If he is innocent, he may count on me. Here is my hand!"

John extended his hand, which Forrester grasped and shook violently. Then Forrester began to search his various pockets, finally coming up with a single guinea piece, which he held out to John.

"Here," he said. "This binds the bargain. It is your retaining fee."

As John walked slowly home that evening he was thinking over the extraordinary scene in his office. He had never found himself in a more embarrassing position. It was well known that he wrote for the *Gazette*, that he was not on the Tory side. Yet here he was, about to defend a captain of the hated Guard. Both sides would loathe him, John told himself miserably.

Yet he knew that he must search out the evidence and defend the soldiers, too, if he found them innocent. It was his duty. Each and every person had the natural right of a fair trial. To have a really fair trial, John decided, the case should be postponed until autumn. Now there would be no chance of justice, only of mob violence.

Immersed in thought, he was startled by a catcall from behind a hedge.

"Lobsters for sale! John Adams, lobsters for sale!" youthful voices shouted. A mud ball hit his cheek with a sting and ran down onto his white cravat, leaving a dark stain. He turned just as his tormentors ran off.

Abigail greeted him almost gaily. "I see you had the attention of the mob, too," she smiled as she wiped the mud from his face and neck.

Then she pointed to a broken window. "They were small stones, and I think the boys must have been small boys," she said.

She held John off at arm's length and surveyed him proudly.

"I saw Josiah Quincy, Jr. He told me what you are going to do. I'm proud of you!"

John took his young wife in his arms.

"Now I shall not need to be ashamed of any miscarriage of justice," she whispered. "I know Captain Preston and the soldiers will have a fair trial."

"You shouldn't have gone out, Abby," John said. "It wasn't safe."

"Oh, I wrapped my big green cape about me. No March wind can get through the folds of that cape."

"You know well I was not referring to March winds," said John soberly. "There are times when a woman should stay at home."

Luckily John was successful in having the trials postponed until fall. And before that time another son, whom they named Charles, was born to them. He was a splendid, healthy baby, and John took a special liking to him from the first week.

John outdid himself at the trials. He carefully filled the jury box with country men, not Bostonians. Then he explained to them the fine points which separate self-defense from murder, and manslaughter from either. Famous author after famous author was quoted; precedent after precedent was described. And finally, after the spirited pleas of Josiah Quincy, Jr. and John's own erudite summing up, Captain Preston and six of the soldiers were acquitted. Two other soldiers were sentenced to be branded in the hand and were thereafter dismissed. But John returned home from the trials feeling far less triumphant than he had expected.

Abigail was always quick to discern his contrary moods. She succeeded in getting him to move the family back to Braintree. There, on his native soil, she hoped John's serenity would be restored.

Yet happiness did not return to John. One night when they were dining with Abigail's elder sister, Polly, who was the wife of his old friend Richard Cranch, John burst out: "There's no more justice left in Britain, Brother Cranch, than there is in hell!"

Cranch had raised his eyebrows at the violence of John's tone of voice, but he said nothing.

"Yes, war is just what they deserve," went on John belligerently. "I could be happy to see the whole Bourbon family on the back of Britain!"

"Why, John!" exclaimed Polly, "I had no idea you were such a firebrand!"

She smoothed down the skirt of her rose silk gown and smiled delightedly at her red-faced brother-in-law.

"Getting to be quite like his cousin Sam, isn't he?" teased Cranch.

To this jibe John bitingly replied, "Don't talk like a Tory, Brother Cranch!" His face flushed deeply; he knew his voice was loud and violent but he could not control it.

"For myself, I could see anything—no matter how terrible—happen to Britain, and rejoice!" he shouted. "If war comes, our clergy will surely pray for them. Then, mayhap, they'll see reason or be ruined!"

Richard Cranch laughed aloud.

"Don't spoil the evening with talk of war and hatred," begged Polly, her eyes flashing with amusement. "Let's have music instead!"

"An excellent idea, Polly," agreed Abigail. "Music is renowned for soothing the savage breast!"

John could see that his wife was displeased. He realized that he was becoming more and more irascible. On the way home Abigail dryly suggested he should see a doctor.

John did, and when he returned from Stafford Springs, Connecticut, where the doctor had ordered him to go for a vacation, he was enthusiastic about the superb scenery along the Connecticut River where he had ridden toward Hartford.

"I wish the Connecticut River flowed through Braintree," he told Abigail. "You should see the rich, fertile fields. It was like paradise. If properly tended, such land can be made to yield two crops!"

"I'm glad you enjoyed yourself," returned Abby. She was well satisfied with the improvement in her husband. Again his cheeks were full of color and his eyes bright. "Now you are pleasant enough to be allowed to hold the new baby." Another son, Thomas Boylston, had been born to them that fall.

When they'd been in Braintree a year and a half and were all feeling happier and healthier, John began to long again for town. Abby agreed to return, so back they moved to Boston in November, to a house on Queen Street.

John was very content. Now that he was disengaged from public affairs, he felt he had nothing to do but mind his law office, his clerks, and his children. He was resolved to avoid politics, political clubs, and town meetings. He meant to spend all his evenings with his family.

Everyone in Massachusetts was happy again and enjoying a prosperity boom. Smuggling was becoming a fine art in Boston!

CHAPTER TWELVE

A FAMOUS TEA PARTY

"Rally Mohawks, bring out your axes,
And tell King George we'll pay no taxes
    On his foreign tea;
His threats are vain, and vain to think
To force our girls and wives to drink
    His vile Bohea!
Then rally, boys, and hasten on
To meet our chiefs at the Green Dragon . . ."

THE GREEN DRAGON INN WAS A TWO-STORY BUILD-
ing with dormer windows in the roof, spacious
and very popular. Its name came from the large
dragon, painted bright green, which topped the wide
entrance door like a huge bird on the wing.

On the night of December 16, 1773, shouting, singing voices broke the quiet of the Boston night. And

115

suddenly the Green Dragon was filled with men painted and dressed like Indians. Where had they come from? everyone wondered. And where were they bound?

John was in Plymouth that night, but he had seen the crowds that had poured into Boston all week. Thousands had met at the Old South Meeting House to hear orators speak on the hated tax of the great East India Company. Placards were plastered on every available wall:

"Friends! Brethren! Gentlemen!

"That worst of plagues, the detested TEA, shipped for this port by the East India Company, has now arrived in this harbor. The hour of destruction, of manly opposition to the machinations of tyranny, stares you in the face. Every friend of his country, to himself and posterity, is now called upon to meet at Faneuil Hall at nine o'clock THIS DAY (at which time the bells will ring) to make a united and successful resistance to this last, worst and most destructive measure of the Administration."

One turnout had been so enormous that only the Old South would hold the crowds. Dr. Thomas Young rose at one meeting and suggested that the only way to get rid of the tea was to throw it overboard. The vessels were not permitted to sail back, nor were they permitted to land their cargoes. Matters had come to an impasse.

The crowd took up the cry. Someone asked how tea

mixed with salt water. Loud, boisterous laughter greeted this sally.

Day followed day that momentous week, until the 16th of December, a Thursday, dawned raw and dreary. A cold rain pelted down from the gray sky.

That evening, Josiah Quincy, who had aided John so splendidly in the trials of Captain Preston and the eight soldiers, spoke vigorously to the crowded assembly:

". . . I see the clouds now arise thick and fast upon our horizon, the thunder roar and the lightning play, and to that God who rides the whirlwind and directs the storm, I commit my country!"

"The hand is to the plough!" a loud voice announced.

"There can be no looking back. We must go forward!" shouted another.

Finally Sam Adams rose and announced quietly that the meeting had done all a meeting could do.

Were his words a signal? Perhaps. For at once, whoops and Indian yells sounded from the doorway, from the gallery. Some fifty men appeared suddenly near the door to the Old South. Each man was wrapped in a blanket, each had his face dyed. A small axe, or tomahawk, was in each man's hand. Where did they come from? The gallery? The Green Dragon? Who knew? Who cared? There they were! It was like a play. They greeted one another hilariously. They grunted Indian fashion, or said in gruff gutturals: "We know you." It was all exciting, and even amusing. Whoops and shouts were taken up by the crowd.

"To Griffin's Wharf!"

"To Griffin's Wharf!"

"To Griffin's Wharf!"

"Boston Harbor will be a teapot tonight!"

Down darkened roads they rushed, more and more men joining them at every bisecting street.

> "Rally Mohawks, bring out your axes,
> And tell King George we'll pay no taxes
> On his foreign tea;
> His threats are vain, and vain to think
> To force our girls and wives to drink
> His vile Bohea!
> Then rally, boys, and hasten on . . ."

Hasten on . . . hasten on . . . there was only the darkness of night in which to accomplish their purpose. They piled aboard the ships from which the watchmen had mysteriously vanished; they swarmed over the sides of the boats, silently rushed along the decks. Almost at once the hatches were off, and case after case of tea was tumbled onto the decks of the vessels.

The *Dartmouth,* the *Beaver,* and the *Eleanor* lay in the dark along the wharf between South Battery and Windmill Point. Sounds of splitting wood, raucous laughter, and loud splashes could be heard along the water front.

All night long the Mohawks worked, and hard work it was. The chests were by no means light, and one after another had to be hoisted upon the bulwarks and turned bottoms up. Paul Revere was there, Sam Adams, John Hancock, and Dr. Warren, too, and many another friend of John Adams.

When John returned the following day and heard

of the tea party, he was delighted. But he was disappointed that he had not taken part in the night's events. He afterwards decided that his cousin Sam had deliberately gotten him away from Boston that night.

"Your cousin Sam was right, John, if he purposely got you away," Abigail insisted. "The Sons of Liberty may need your legal services."

Suddenly her eyes shone. "Oh, John, it was wonderful! Painted hands and arms broke tea chest after tea chest and dumped them overboard until the shore was strewn with tea leaves for miles, almost up to our

Braintree beaches. You must have seen the Bohea, you must have smelt it, as you rode up from Plymouth! What a shame Dr. Warren had to leave before you arrived!"

"Oh, Portia, you need not think I admire this effort of the patriots less than you do! I only wish I hadn't missed Dr. Warren's visit. I should have enjoyed a firsthand account of the occasion."

John was beaming with satisfaction. "It was magnificent; there was a dignity, a sublimity to it," he burst out in extravagant language. "A sublimity positively lyrical!"

Abigail smiled. Yes, it was like an epic poem, she thought. What a pity John couldn't at least have seen his friends marching back from the docks to fife and drum, stopping en route to serenade Admiral Montague at his lodgings in town.

"Yes, John," she agreed aloud, "it is like a poem but not lyrical; tragical rather. I tremble for the consequences the baneful weed will bring to our country, your country and mine, John. I would not express my fears to anyone else."

"My dearest Portia, you need not tremble for yourself or me," John answered, "though, mayhap, for our children. They may see a revolution. But today, as you know, the people are trimmers, just as they've been for the past ten years. First they hate England; then they are in love with the mother country again."

"It depends on how their pockets are affected, methinks."

"Well it may, Abigail," John said soberly. "When there are children's mouths to feed, it is necessary to consider such matters."

"Ah, yes, my dear husband, but what are full mouths without freedom? I fancy the gorge would rise in you as well as me. There is no looking backward anymore."

"Even as things are now, I can't earn a living in Boston," John said. "We must return to Braintree. Since I bought the homestead, where I was born, from my brother, it would be well if I try to make it pay. I don't propose to let my children starve for freedom or for any reason."

"You know you always wanted the house for sentimental reasons," Abigail smiled at John. "Those fifty acres with the meandering brook make you lyrical whenever you mention them. I've come to know well that light in your eyes! Yes, it will be better for the children, too, if we return to the country."

"With the courts all closed, I have no choice . . ."

"It is a small price to pay for liberty and freedom," observed Abigail reasonably. "Moreover you are fortunate. You love your farm. I'm beginning to agree with your cousin Sam and Dr. Warren that complete independence and freedom for our country is the only solution to present troubles."

So back to Braintree went the Adams family. However, in June, 1774, John allowed the Sons of Liberty to lure him from the farm to act as moderator at a meeting in Faneuil Hall.

For a fortnight and more before this meeting, John and Abigail, in common with most of the inhabitants of Braintree and Boston, had vehemently discussed the "Five Intolerable Acts" which the British Parliament had passed to punish the Bostonians for giving such an expensive tea party. The tea party had cost the East India Company eighty thousand pounds; this had enraged the Londoners. It was voted almost unanimously in the British Commons to "punish that nest of locusts" in Boston.

The Bostonians might smile at the name-calling of the British Parliament, but they did not smile at the order to close the port of Boston. No vessel could enter or leave the harbor except on Crown business; even the ferry to Charlestown was forbidden to operate. A man could not even go out by boat to catch a mess of fish to feed his family. How could merchants carry on their trades? How could any business survive?

Boston went into mourning. The bells tolled. The streets were strangely deserted.

The towns of Salem and Marblehead, which had been designated by England as the "new ports," were old rivals of Boston. Now they showed that they were no trimmers. They freely offered the Boston commerce the use of their docks and ports.

Sam Adams had not been idle. When the first news of the "Intolerable Acts" reached Boston he started sending circular letters to other colonists. These resolutions, drawn up with members from Charlestown, Cambridge, Brookline, Newton, Dorchester, Roxbury, Lexington, and Lynn, proclaimed:

"This attack, though made immediately on us, is doubtless designed for every other colony who shall not surrender their sacred rights and liberties into the hands of the infamous Ministry. Now, therefore, is the time when ALL should be united in opposition to this violation of the liberties of all.

"The people receive the edict with indignation. It is

expected by their enemies and feared by some of their friends that the town will not be able to support the cause under so severe a trial . . ."

Paul Revere rode about the country delivering this correspondence; even to towns as distant as Philadelphia and New York, he rode.

Philadelphia suggested a congress to express sympathy and decide on assistance for Boston.

Meanwhile "Lord North's Coasters," as the wagons which plied from Marblehead and Salem to the relief of stricken Boston were called, brought some assistance. Yet starvation faced the city, just as the King's Minister, Lord North, King George III himself, and the British House of Commons hoped and expected when they passed the "Five Intolerable Acts."

Fortunately for Massachusetts, the other colonies refused to stand calmly by in this emergency.

Old Israel Putnam of Connecticut drove a flock of sheep to Boston; Philadelphia sent money; Baltimore, more realistically, sent bread and grain.

Even London, England, sent money!

Alexandria, down in Virginia, where they kept a fast day to honor Boston, sent money and flour. And old Christopher Gadsden sent a heartening message with a shipload of rice, the gift of South Carolina's lowland planters.

"Don't pay for an ounce of the damn tea!" he said.

After the fifth of the "Intolerables" was enforced, Virginia, too, was involved in the rebellion. Neither she nor Pennsylvania had any intention of permitting Canadians to colonize their western borders.

Young Colonel George Washington of the Virginia

Militia, in addressing the House of Burgesses, said: "If need be I will raise one thousand men, subsist them at my own expense, and march myself at their head to the relief of Boston."

John Adams, too, in his way, helped to save Boston.

At the Faneuil Hall meeting Josiah Quincy suggested that common tables be instituted to feed the Boston poor, many of them near to starvation due to unemployment since the stoppage of trade. He went on to advise that those present in Faneuil Hall pay for this out of their own pockets. The mood of the meeting changed quickly. No's and boos echoed to the rafters of the famous hall.

John Adams stepped to the front of the platform. He was almost too angry to speak. His face was red and his hands were clenched in tight knots, when he managed to pour forth some of his disgust:

"John Milton, the English poet you all know, had proper words to describe the members of this meeting," he said in a harsh, surly voice. "He wrote them in his Twelfth Sonnet:

" 'Owls and cuckoos, asses, apes and dogs . . .' "

Again the mood of the crowd suddenly shifted. Laughter, hearty and genial, greeted John's sally.

He rapped for order. "Now," he said, "we will consider the motion for Common Tables."

General Gage and his regiments had taken the place of the hated Hutchinson. Boston knew she could not face England alone. John knew this as well as did his cousin Sam and all the Sons of Liberty, who this very afternoon were in Salem putting through the Massachusetts Congress a motion for a General Congress in Philadelphia. Secrecy was essential, yet Tory spies managed to smuggle into the meeting. Hence the order went out promptly that no future meeting could be held. This, of June 17, 1774, was the last Provincial Assembly to convene in the state of Massachusetts under Royal Authority.

The end was almost in sight.

This Assembly, as its last act, appointed a committee of five to go to Philadelphia in September.

John Adams was one of the five delegates selected.

CHAPTER THIRTEEN

"ATLAS OF INDEPENDENCE"

O N AUGUST 10, 1774, FOUR OF THE DELEGATES
assembled at the home of Thomas Cushing.
John and Sam Adams, as well as Robert Treat
Paine, arrived on time. But the fifth delegate was de-
tained at home because his wife was ill.

The wives of the delegates were there, too, and they
were worried. It was a gloomy occasion. How well
Abigail, who was by now nearly thirty years old, realized the impending dangers. John had often been away
from home, on circuit, but never had he gone as far
as Philadelphia.

Would she ever see her beloved husband again? she
asked herself. Men died on the scaffold who dared defy
the British sovereigns! She wouldn't want to live if
anything happened to John. What would become of
the children? Abby clenched her hands, determined

126

to show no sign of emotion to disturb John. He was depressed enough without the addition of a weeping wife.

Never had John Adams felt so inadequate, so uncertain of his own ability.

Outside the Cushing house in Boston a crowd had gathered. They were shouting: "Sam Adams! Sam Adams!"

It was time to leave for Philadelphia. John walked over to Abigail, who was sitting with Mrs. Sam Adams. He took both her hands in his and pressed them. Then he bent and whispered in her ear. Before she could realize it, he was gone. The men were getting into the coach. The crowd was now shouting:

"John Adams! Sam Adams! Hurrah for the Congress!"

Five British regiments were encamped on Boston Common. The coach and four of the delegates was "preceded by two white servants well-mounted and armed, with four blacks in livery, two on horseback and two footmen."

John uttered a silent prayer to God that he might not fail in the part he had been called upon to play.

The first stage of the journey through Massachusetts and Connecticut was a continuous ovation. But when they reached New York no salutes were fired; men, women, and children didn't crowd about the coach in great numbers.

John was shocked by New York people. He found they had a way of talking "very fast, very loud and altogether"! He met all the important people. Peter Van Brugh Livingston, a retired merchant who was not impressed with the importance of Boston, told John that he thought Bostonians had acted like so many Goths and Vandals. John flushed in anger, but before he could frame a suitable retort, the New Yorker was observing that Bostonians had even hung Quakers! John was appalled; such matters of the past he thought best ignored.

He was more content in Princeton, where they attended prayers at the college and talked pleasantly with the Scotch president, Dr. Witherspoon, whom John found "as high a Son of Liberty as any in America."

The delegates were three weeks en route. By the time they crossed the Delaware River and reached Philadelphia they were soiled and travel worn; even the fine new clothes his Boston friends had given Sam Adams looked worse for the wear.

When they finally were settled at the home of Miss Jane Port on Arch Street, John was so agitated that he couldn't sleep. They had heard rumors that the gunpowder in Boston had been seized and that the fleet and General Gage's troops were firing on the town. What would happen to Abby? What of little Abby, Johnny, Charles, and baby Tommy? It suddenly occurred to John that he should never have left his own family, that his place was with them.

But was it? his conscience demanded. Must not he and every man put duty to his country first? So he tossed and even wept that first night in Philadelphia.

The following morning the delegates from the thirteen colonies, some fifty of them, assembled in Carpenters' Hall.

This was a harmonious new building of brick, only

recently opened. It was the pride of the Carpenters, who built every inch of it, from the foundations to the graceful cupola which topped it. Classic in style, its second-story windows were long, curved at the top, supported by small white columns. A broad flight of steps led to the exquisitely proportioned doorway, with square pillars on either side. Inside, the hallway ran through the building to a beautiful fanlighted doorway at the rear. This was the architectural triumph of the building. On either side of the hallway were perfectly proportioned rooms. To the west there was a library.

The members met in the east room, where the warm September sun poured in. There was a desk for the chairman, and rows of hickory armchairs for the delegates. A small room, John thought, as he sat down between his cousin Sam and Mr. Cushing.

. Day after day, week after week, he sat here, sometimes arising to talk to the delegates but more often listening. Night after night, after the meetings, he was entertained to such sumptuous meals as he had never deemed possible, most "sinful feasts," John thought, of "turtle, flummery, jellies, sweetmeats of twenty sorts, almonds, raisins," melons "fine beyond description," excellent peaches, pears, and wine. Even the Quakers entertained him to "ducks, hams, chickens, beef, pigs, tarts, creams, custards, jellies, fools, trifles, floating islands."

Philadelphia was a *city*. As John toured about and viewed the skeletons and waxworks of one doctor, the anatomical charts of another, and visited the hospital where lunatics were kept in an underground room, his astonishment grew. And what bookshops! John could have happily spent all his time in them. It seemed to him that Boston was actually only a village.

He wrote Abigail of the eloquence he heard in Carpenters' Hall: "The art and address of Ambassadors from a dozen belligerent powers of Europe, nay, of a conclave of Cardinals at an election of a Pope, or of the Princes in Germany at the choice of an Emperor, would not exceed the specimens we have seen and heard."

Yet after a few weeks John was writing his wife in a different way:

"I'm wearied to death with the life I lead. The business of the Congress is tedious beyond expression . . . I believe that if it was moved and seconded that we should come to a resolution that three and two make five, we should be entertained with logic and rhetoric, law, history, politics, and mathematics, and then—we should pass the resolution unanimously in the affirmative."

John felt nothing had really been accomplished, that the delegates were timid and irresolute, with the exception of a few from Virginia and New England.

A memory that John particularly cherished was that of Patrick Henry, interrupting a Virginian colleague to insist:

"We must vote by poll *not* by colonies! To vote by colonies will defeat the purpose of the Congress. Where are now your landmarks, your boundaries of colonies? The distinction between Virginians, Pennsylvanians, New Yorkers, New Englanders, are no more. *I am not a Virginian but an American!*"

Though he was only thirty-nine, John felt like an

old man when he left Philadelphia to return home for Thanksgiving. He only took heart again when he reached New England, where he saw great military preparations being made everywhere. At any rate, they had voted in Philadelphia to convene again next year. He tried to console himself with that; it was a step forward, if a very small one.

It had all been a great experience for John Adams, but he asked nothing of the future but to remain on his Braintree farm with his wife and children. It was better for a man to be home in times like these. His family and Boston had need of him.

Yet as the winter went on John realized more and more that there was no turning back. He was even ready to go again to Philadelphia if needed there. In April of 1775, when the battles of Lexington and Concord made the 18th forever famous, he knew there was no way to avoid further bloodshed. He rode to Cambridge a few days after the battles and found the little army "in great confusion and much distress." He rode soberly home that night.

After the children were in bed he turned to Abigail:

"The die is cast, the Rubicon is passed . . ."

"May we all prove Caesars in the coming years," said Abigail with resolution.

"Yes." John looked dour. "As Lord Mansfield expressed it in Parliament, if we do not defend ourselves they will kill us."

"They may kill us, many of us," retorted Abigail, "but if we have spirit and resolution they will never conquer us!"

The next day John came down with a raging fever. Abigail was frightened, but she nursed him tenderly

and soon he was strong enough to start out for Philadelphia. He traveled in a sulky, with a servant accom-
panying him on horseback, and overtook his fellow
members of the coming Congress. This time John Hancock was with them.

The late spring and early summer John worked hard,
despite the heat of Philadelphia and the sad news
from home. The battle of Bunker's Hill was fought that
June, and Dr. Warren, the family physician, was
killed. Little Johnny Adams was inconsolable. He wept
and vowed to revenge his doctor; he wept again and
swore vengeance against all the British. Little Abby
cried and cried.

Both of John's brothers now had commissions in the
army, as had Abigail's brother, William. John, too,
felt he must *fight*.

Next came news of the terrible plague of dysentery.
His merry brother Elihu died; his own son, baby
Tommy, was desperately ill; young and old were dying like flies. It was especially distressing to be separated from Abigail and the children at this time.

But there was so much work for him to do in Philadelphia. The Congress now sat in the State House on
Chestnut Street. This larger building, in the Georgian
manner, was the pride of the Philadelphians. The
Congress had a large room on the east end; this white-
panelled conference hall had windows on both sides
and was equipped with twin fireplaces.

Dr. Benjamin Franklin, who had just landed from
England, now joined the other members of the Congress. John managed to put through his nomination
of George Washington of Virginia as General-in-chief

of the Armies of the Colonies. Many opposed it, but it was finally carried by a majority vote.

Tired but triumphant he returned to his rooms that hot night to learn of the death of Josiah Quincy; he had died on the boat that was bringing him home from his hopeless mission to London. "Dear Josiah, so true and so brave," John murmured to himself.

At the same time he learned that his old friend Jonathan Sewall had fled to England. "Poor Jonathan, so debonair yet so deluded," John sighed. His friends were gone forever, as was his gay younger brother. Pain, loss, and misery were on every hand.

Nor did the fall and winter bring better news. Everything in the Philadelphia Congress moved with maddening slowness. Abigail wrote from Boston that prices had doubled, that her house was constantly filled with refugees from the British guns. Cousin Sam's son had been thrown into prison by the British; there was a price on Sam's head now. A cold shiver went down John's spine. Where would it end?

There were Loyalists on every hand, in every family. How could the colonies free themselves when so many persons were indifferent and so many more opposed to revolting against the King of England?

In February, 1776, John was appointed Chief Justice of the Superior Court of Massachusetts; that spring, too, the question of assistance from France came up. Patrick Henry was alarmed for fear England would offer France half of the North American continent if she would assist in subduing the colonies. Everyone was agitated, arguing this way and that. John was afraid of French entanglements. He wanted no foreign power on American soil. Yet he knew the colonies must have help.

Still nothing could be done until the colonies themselves had declared their independence from the mother country. John now devoted all his efforts to bringing this about.

"Whereas his Britannic Majesty, in conjunction with the lords and commons of Great Britain, has, by a late act of Parliament, excluded the inhabitants of these United Colonies from the protection of his crown; And whereas no answer, whatever, to the humble petitions of the colonies for redress of grievances and reconciliation with Great Britain, has been or is likely to be given; but, the whole force of that kingdom, aided by foreign mercenaries, is to be exerted for the destruction of the good people of these colonies; And whereas it appears absolutely irreconcilable to reason and good Conscience, for the people of these colonies now to take the oaths and affirmations necessary for the support of any government under the crown of Great Britain, and it is necessary that the exercise of every kind of authority under the said crown should be totally suppressed, and all the powers of government exerted, under the authority of the people of the colonies, for the preservation of internal peace, virtue, and good order, as well as for the defence of their lives, liberties, and properties, against the hostile invasion and cruel depredations of their enemies . . ."

John reread what he had written and decided that the Preamble and Resolve expressed exactly what he wanted it to express. He arose in Congress with it in his hands on that 15th of May, filled with a calm satisfaction.

He read what he had written.

Almost before he had uttered the last word, cries of

"I protest!" "I protest!" rang out. Finally, after long discussions, the measure was accepted by a good majority. It was a personal triumph for John.

He was elated. But only to his dear Portia would he admit it! To her he wrote: "When I consider the great events which are passed, and those greater which are rapidly advancing, and that I may have been instrumental in touching some small springs and turning some small wheels, which have had and will have such effects, I feel an awe upon my mind which is not easily described."

Even a month later unanimity had not been obtained among the delegates. Yet so important was the French alliance by then that a document was presented to the Congress which stated:

"That these colonies are and of right ought to be free and independent States, that they are absolved from all allegiance with the British Crown, and that all political connection between them and the state of Great Britain is, and ought to be, totally dissolved.

"That it is expedient forthwith to take the most effectual measures for forming foreign alliances . . ."

By now John was working on the document with Dr. Benjamin Franklin, Thomas Jefferson of Virginia, and Roger Sherman of Connecticut.

To John, happiness and virtue were closely allied. Hadn't all sober inquirers after truth, ancient and modern, pagan and Christian, declared that the happiness of man, as well as his dignity, consisted in virtue? Confucius, the famous Chinese sage; Zoroaster, the great Persian teacher who lived eight hundred

years before Christ; Socrates, the Greek philosopher who was the teacher of Plato; Mohammed, whose *Koran* was the Bible of all Islam; and the sacred writers of Christianity were all agreed on this. Consequently, it seemed plain to John that the Republican form of government, which rests on virtue, as Montesquieu, the French philosophical historian, had shown, was the best possible form.

The final form of the Declaration of Independence was not agreed upon until July 4, 1776. John made a splendid speech in its favor earlier in the month. Wherever he went he was now hailed as "the Atlas of independence" and "the Colossus of debate." It was very pleasant, John thought, to have his efforts at last recognized.

Then it was time for the delegates to vote on the declaration. On July 2, John Dickinson and Robert Morris stayed away; James Wilson voted Aye and brought Pennsylvania over. But still Caesar Rodney of Delaware had not arrived. Could they muster a majority without him? Edward Rutledge brought South Carolina around. John Hancock, on signing the declaration, wrote his name in a very large hand, exclaiming:

"There, I guess King George will be able to read that!"

But why didn't Caesar Rodney come?

Riding through mud and rain as never man rode before, eighty miles through deep darkness, his horse frothing at the mouth, at last "the tall, thin, pale man, with a face no bigger than an apple" was in the State House yard!

Never was "the oddest-looking fellow in the world"

more welcome to John. Caesar Rodney of Delaware
had the deciding vote!

This was "a man of sense, fire, spirit, wit and hu-
mor," as John knew well. He would not let the American patriots down! He was one with them.

So little Delaware joined her fellow colonies.
Twelve states had at last voted Aye and New York
was assured. Hadn't Henry Wisner promised it? Any-
how, it was well known that New York could not
stand alone.

John was exhausted from all the fears and excitement of those trying days. He knew that on July 2nd
and 4th monumental work had been done. He felt
assured that July 4 was a day which would be honored
through the generations.

That hot summer in Philadelphia John was chairman of the Board of War and Ordnance, equivalent
to Minister of War. He worked from dawn well past
midnight week after week, month after month. The
monotonous routine was dreary. The confinement was
beginning to affect his health.

What a bulwark Abigail's letters were! With sick
children about her, she was undaunted by lies and
rumors. When the smallpox ravage reached frighten-
ing proportions, she shepherded her brood into Boston and had them and herself inoculated! She raised
and husked corn and even dug potatoes and milked
the cows. Help was unobtainable. There was apparently nothing that John's dear Portia could not do.

But by fall John was worn out mentally and physi-
cally. He needed a rest, and it was granted him. He
set off for home with a happy heart.

How proud he was of nine-year-old Johnny who

rode to and from Boston with post and messages!
What a fine girl, what a handsome girl Abby was at
eleven! And Charles and Tommy were no less lova-
ble. It was good, so good it brought tears to his tired
eyes, to be home in Braintree again.

Yet he agreed to serve another year with the Congress. But that should be the last, the very last.

"I certainly hope it will," Abigail said fervently. "Yet
methinks you will stay more than a year if needed."
She raised her bright eyes from her sewing. "I can
manage here. It is lonely, but my family and relatives
live near and I have the children."

"The war will be long," John insisted gloomily.

"Probably it will, although I think General Lee no
loss, even if the British have gotten him back. I am
delighted at General Washington's sally against the
Hessians in Trenton. They'll sing their *lieder* to another
tune now, methinks!"

"Yes, that was a fearful slaughter," John agreed.

"It's kill or be killed now," said Abigail calmly, as
she went on with her darning.

"Washington was clever to surprise them at Princeton, too," John admitted. "But he never seems to con-
solidate his victories. I doubt the war will be over in
ten years."

Abigail frowned. After a few minutes she looked
very carefully at her husband. "You must be tired,"
she observed. "It is not patriotic, nor sensible, to harbor such gloomy thoughts."

"Perhaps my gloom is due to my leaving you tomorrow," John said, still rather sourly.

Abigail laughed. "Why, you sound almost like you
did years ago when you were courting me!"

When he rode off the next day, Abigail sat down and had a good cry. She had been brave as steadily as she could, for John's sake. Now she gave way, but not for long. There was work to be done, a farm to be managed, four children to be cared for and educated. As all the schools were closed, she had to teach the children herself, with the exception of Johnny, who was being tutored by her husband's clerk, John Thaxter.

After what John called "a march like Hannibal's over the Alps" he rode into Fishkill, New York, on his new colt. He crossed the Hudson at Poughkeepsie on the ice and the Delaware at Easton likewise. It was February when he arrived in Baltimore, where he awaited his colleagues in the Continental Congress.

CHAPTER FOURTEEN

"STAY HOME FOR GOOD"

BALTIMORE PROVED TO BE A DELIGHTFUL TOWN;
for four or five weeks John enjoyed himself
almost every minute. Then the Congress returned to Philadelphia. For John the city seemed
changed. As he himself put it: "More than one half of
the inhabitants have removed into the country . . . the
remainder are chiefly Quakers, as dull as beetles." It
is probable that at this time John was not popular
with the peace-loving element of Philadelphia!

So dreary week followed dreary week, and dull
month followed dull month. John's work at the Congress was far less confining than it had been. He
longed for home and vowed that at the end of this trying year he would "stay home for good."

Nor was the war news heartening. There had never
been a gloomier period. By the end of August two of

141

his fellow members were ill of a raging fever. Luckily John had no fear of catching this serious disorder; his illnesses, as he observed, were "more chronical, nervous and slow." He was occupied, as so often at this time, with arguments with his fellow members of Congress.

General John Sullivan had come to Congress with a message from Sir William Howe's brother, Lord Richard Howe. His lordship desired a brief talk with members of Congress "in their private capacities."

John was chosen to accompany Dr. Benjamin Franklin to the meeting, where Lord Howe said he "loved" America, that he "hated to see her deflowered of her splendid manhood" in a war she could not possibly win. His lordship went on to say that the good King George III was prepared to take the colonists back into his graces if they would give up fighting.

"The generous King," continued Lord Howe, "will grant everything within reason that the colonists should ask for."

John's face flushed darkly; he glanced at the imperturbable Dr. Franklin, who appeared to be more amused than irritated.

"Only if the generous King will recognize the Independence of the United States can an armistice be considered," said Dr. Franklin, who acted as spokesman. His voice was so gentle and he spoke so pleasantly that John wondered if Lord Howe would be suitably impressed. He was not impressed; he was irritated.

"But that would be impossible, Dr. Franklin! Well you must know this is an impossible condition." Lord Howe tried to keep his voice conversational. "I am sorry you can give me no ground to hope for peace."

His lordship smiled, not pleasantly.

Dr. Franklin smiled pleasantly. "I am sorry, too, my lord," he said quietly.

The private meeting was at an end; it had come to nothing, just as John had thought it would when he originally opposed it.

This was the overture to Sir William Howe's drive on Philadelphia.

In the early morning hours of September 19, 1777, the members of Congress were aroused from their sleep to learn that Sir William Howe had driven General Washington's men before him. That even Lafayette and Pulaski, both of whom made superhuman efforts, could not rally the fleeing Americans. Sir William was crossing the Brandywine River and would be in Philadelphia that evening!

What a rush there was! The precious recorded minutes of the Continental Congress were of first concern. As John remarked dryly, the papers were of more importance than the lives of the members!

At last the exodus was well under way. They fled through Trenton, Easton, and Bethlehem to Reading on the Schuylkill River. Here they rested briefly. The town was well defended, as there was a military dump situated there. On the other hand it was a desirable catch for the enemy for the same reason, so the members of Congress soon departed, halting next at Lancaster.

John was tired and dirty, his journey still far from complete. But his spirits revived somewhat as they journeyed through the fertile country to the shores of the Susquehanna River. Here were fat cattle, barns overflowing with grain, friendly farmers. This Pennsylvania countryside was enough to enchant the heart of the Braintree farmer which lurked just below the surface of John Adams.

He became almost gay after they crossed the river, a mile broad at that point, and rode along the pathway to York.

"Howe won't gain much getting Philadelphia," he observed to his companion. "Perhaps they'll feed him so well he'll forget to fight."

"Humph!" returned Mr. Marchant of Rhode Island. "I rather expected reverses at first. But when we hear from our New England men, you'll hear a different tune."

As they rode along they saw orchards bowed to the ground with reddening apple crops. The people of the countryside, as plump as their cattle, came out to greet the members of Congress.

At last they arrived in York. John, his cousin Sam, and Mr. Gerry were guests in the home of General Roberdeau, an Israelite whose family and servants could not do enough to make them comfortable. John was delighted to find his linens promptly laundered and mended, his suits pressed and cleaned, warm water when needed, and ample quantities of well-cooked food. He had not anticipated such a welcome; surely he was better situated than John Hancock, who, as President of the Congress, had had first choice of residence. If Abigail and the children could have been there John would have been content.

The precious papers of the Congress had been secreted. The members held meetings in the Courthouse, a small brick building where town affairs were conducted.

John occasionally took time off to hunt or fish with elderly local sportsmen, or he would walk about the town and talk with various people who could speak English. Here even the schools were conducted in the German language, he discovered. How could these various nationalities be molded into Americans, he asked himself, when they still clung to their old European languages and customs? It depressed him.

One morning when he was having breakfast at General Roberdeau's, Reverend Nicholas Kurtz, minister of the Christ Lutheran Church, came to see the General. John had heard that the minister was collecting clothes for the suffering soldiers.

Reverend Kurtz sat down at the table and had a cup of coffee.

"How do you like our little town, Mr. Adams?" Reverend Kurtz asked, smiling at John.

"It's a pleasant change for me," John said. "You have fine farms hereabouts."

"Indeed we do!" the local pastor agreed. "Have you seen the Rankin plantation? We still call it that, though the family has fled to England and my daughter-in-law runs it for her father, Captain Albright, when he is fighting at the front."

"You have heard of Captain Philip Albright," said a member of the General's family who had come in with second cups of coffee. "I told you the other night that when he was taken prisoner, he was put on an old ship in the Delaware River and how he escaped by night!"

"I do recall it now," said John. "He was the soldier who swam the Brandywine, placing his watch on a log to keep it from the water, wasn't he? I remember it particularly," he continued, turning to the pastor, "because I was struck by his providence. It had a hint of our New England thrift."

"We Americans are all much alike," said Reverend Kurtz. "If you would care to meet Captain Philip Albright I can take you out to his mill one day. He is there at present. His miller regularly takes the flour to Philadelphia in great wagons, where George Latimer attends to its sale."

"I hope he isn't filling the stomachs of Howe's men while our own soldiers go hungry." John spoke rather sourly. It was a sore point with him that some Americans put trade before patriotism.

Reverend Kurtz tried to control his irritation. But as he rose to go, he held out his hand to John and said: "We are very patriotic here in York, I can assure you. Why, take Killian Small, one of our most prosperous farmers with a fine carpentry business! He gave up all this and enlisted as soon as he heard of the battles of Lexington, Concord, and Bunker Hill."

John was abashed. He had let his temper get the better of him. He must exercise more control in the future, he told himself as he settled back in his chair and asked for paper and ink that he might write Abigail.

If he could only get home for good! He needed the close friendship of his wife, he wanted his own children about him, not these strange children whom he met on every corner.

After the girl brought the writing materials she

lingered to remark, "I'm glad you met our York pastor. He was the first Lutheran minister ordained by a synod in America, you know. He had a lot of trouble over his oath of allegiance to King George III, but last year he came out on our side and he is as loyal as any man today!"

York had been "soaking and poaching" in the heaviest rain in years and this increased John's gloom. He wondered how Tom Paine ever managed to write that inspiriting pamphlet, "The American Crisis," here. If only there could be one bit of cheering news from the fighting men!

But day after day there was nothing but bad news.

Then came the glorious day when a rider galloped down the crowded main street of little York. Dismounting at the Courthouse steps, he burst into the session of Congress, removing his hat as he hurried to the desk of John Hancock, the President. From a leather bag he took a sealed letter and handed it to Hancock. But the messenger could not wait for the seal to be broken. He turned to the members and shouted:

"Burgoyne has surrendered to Gates!"

Instantaneously the Congress rose to its feet. There was deafening applause. Everyone rushed to shake the hand of the excited, travel-soiled soldier who had brought this marvelous news. Everyone talked at once and bombarded the soldier with questions.

John could hardly contain his elation. Victory at last! A great victory, and won by the men of New England!

It took two of the bloodiest battles of the year, one on September 19, another on October 7, before General Burgoyne finally surrendered on October 17,

1777, at Freeman's farm. It was a major setback for the British and a turning point of the war. More than anything, it aided the Americans in securing the essential military and financial assistance from the enemies of the British.

John felt that he was no longer needed at the Congress. He had been gone for over a year when, in November, he and Sam Adams set out on horseback for home.

For nineteen days they rode Bostonward, and every hoofbeat sang to John: "Home for good, home for good!" Often he turned to his cousin and said, "I'm going home for good!"

Sam never answered, and John could not understand his enigmatic smile. John meant what he said. He was going home for good.

And good it was to be home! How wonderful his farm looked! Even so late in the season he could see its splendid condition. What a hearty Thanksgiving it was, almost like the earlier ones. How the children had grown!

One night in December, after the children were in bed, John said to Abigail:

"Your father at seventy is healthy, but I can see how lonely he is without your mother. The children, too, suffered a great loss in her death. After the influence of mother and father, that of the grandmother is the most important in young lives. Your mother, dear Portia, was so able to teach benevolence and charity, industry and virtue, in private life," observed John, "that her loss greatly increases your own burden."

"I have done the best I could with Abby and the boys," Abigail murmured.

"John Quincy has genius, and so has Charles!" John spoke with enthusiasm. "But we must take care they do not go astray; we must cultivate their minds, inspire their hearts. We must root out every meanness, make them great and manly. Teach them to scorn falsehood, injustice, cowardice, and ingratitude."

"I have done this to the best of my ability, my dear," Abigail said. "I do not think you can complain."

"Complain! I had no such thought, as you must know." John was perturbed.

"Perhaps I used the wrong word," returned Abigail demurely. "I know I have labored with all four of them to instil naturalness and grace in all their movements, to adapt their ears to music and the sound of various intonations in the human speaking voice. You should hear how wonderfully Johnny reads aloud!"

"This winter he shall read to me and next winter! The next, Charles shall read to me, and then Tommy." The future would be full of joy, John told himself, because he was home, home for good.

But the very next day Johnny brought from Boston a large packet from the Congress, addressed to his father. John broke the seals and bent over Abigail to share the news with her.

John Adams had been appointed, with Dr. Franklin and Mr. Lee, a plenipotentiary to France! He knew at once that he could not refuse. It was his duty to go. But he could not bear to go alone.

So he decided to take his oldest son, John Quincy, with him.

"Not Johnny!" Abigail protested.

"It is a great chance for the boy to learn French," John insisted. "There is no time but youth when a foreign language can be well learned. You would not stand in the way of his education, I'm sure."

Abigail shook her head. She felt numb. Now she would be alone again, this time with twelve-year-old Abby and the two younger boys.

"Take me with you," she begged. "Take Abby and me. She, too, should learn French. The younger children can stay with relatives."

"Why, that's impossible!" John was amazed at the suggestion. "You know how dangerous it is to cross the Atlantic in these war times, how unsuitable for women and girls! I will be gone only a short time; then I shall be home for good."

So on a cold February day in 1778, John and his oldest son climbed from Braintree's pebbled shore into a ship's boat. They were both wrapped in blankets, their feet encased in hay to protect them from the bitter cold. The wind whistled about their reddened ears as they were rowed out to the frigate, *Boston*.

Scarcely had the frigate left Massachusetts Bay when a squadron of British warships set out in pursuit. For two days and nights it was touch and go. John put all his important papers in a package and prepared to drop it overboard if he was captured. If it had not been for Johnny, he would have considered following his package into the deep. He had no taste for a British prison.

Then the *Boston* sailed into a frightful storm. For days and days everyone aboard was violently sick. At midnight a bolt of lightning struck the mast. Some sailors were knocked unconscious and some twenty of the crew were injured.

Before John could recover from the storm the *Boston* met a British privateer and a fight ensued. A cannon ball whisked close to John's head and carried away the ship's spanker yard. Throughout these violent happenings Johnny had been cheerful and helpful, to John's pride and delight.

The Atlantic Ocean was the scene of constant combat. The *Boston* managed at times to take rich prizes. On one occasion the first lieutenant was hit, and John held him while the surgeon amputated his wounded leg. A fortnight later they buried the man at sea.

Johnny bore himself steadily and well through the weeks. He left no inch of the frigate unexplored, but climbed everywhere. While John made himself a second to the captain as it were, Johnny enjoyed the journey in his own way.

At last they landed safely and Johnny was placed in a French school with Dr. Franklin's sons and two other American lads. He was already more of a diplomat than his father. He managed to escape Mass on Sundays and increase the play days for himself and his friends.

As soon as John reached Dr. Franklin's house in Passy he learned that the purpose of his trip—the treaties of commerce and alliance—had been accomplished before he left Braintree's pebbled beaches! Not only had France signed the treaties on February 6, 1778; she had also recognized the independence of the United States and declared war on England.

John decided to stay on. He enjoyed the French theater and was himself studying the French language.

Everything interested him, though not the drawn-out social functions. These he found simply dull.

When Dr. Franklin drove into Paris daily, John would remain in Passy, quietly studying, reading, or visiting the few French friends he had in the neighborhood. He was chagrined that no one seemed to consider him or his opinions of any importance. They all went to Dr. Franklin, who spoke the language like a native.

At the end of a year John could stand his equivocal position no longer. He decided to return home. This time it would be for good. He had seen the world now and was only too anxious to settle down on his own Braintree acres.

The return journey was far different from his February crossing. Not only was he accompanied by the French Ambassador and his elegant suite dressed in full court regalia, but he was on a French ship, the *Sensible,* escorted by a goodly portion of the French fleet.

Johnny was the delight of the passengers. John basked in the compliments which he received about his brilliant son. He could hardly wait to see the other children, too.

He wrote an old friend that "a retreat infinitely less splendid than that of Pythagoras, at the head of a little school to teach a few children the elements of knowledge, would be a kind of heaven."

Yes, and it was like heaven to be home again. Now he would stay home for good, he vowed, as he grasped Abigail and his children in his arms.

"Oh, my dear, dear friend," Abigail's eyes shone but she found it difficult to speak. How lonely had been her days! How lonely had been the long nights! What fears had oppressed her!

"Promise me, John, promise me that you will never leave me alone with the children again," she begged.

John looked at her troubled face with surprise. She was trying to smile through her tears.

"This isn't like my Portia," John said tenderly. "Of course, I shall never leave you again. This is our home. The war will not last forever, now that we have good foreign alliances. I have come home for good."

CHAPTER FIFTEEN

MINISTER TO HOLLAND AND
MINISTER TO ENGLAND

IN SEPTEMBER JOHN BEGAN WRITING A CONSTITU-
tion for his native state. The famous Massachusetts Bill of Rights, which anticipated that in the
federal Constitution, was largely the work of John
Adams.

It was a joy to labor with and for the men of his
own community; it was an additional joy to have
at hand his old library, to which he had recently added
many books, especially on government, secured abroad.
When the Constitution was finally adopted, he boasted
to Abigail:

154

"We took every precaution that wise people jealous of their liberties could take. No government was ever made so perfectly on the principle of the people's rights and equality. It is Locke, Sidney, Rousseau, and de Mably reduced to practice for the first time."

"Do you recall how we read John Locke together before we married?" Abigail's eyes shone. She was wondrously proud of her husband. "Not until recently did I read Jean Jacques Rousseau's *Social Contract* or learn of the work of the Abbé de Mably. Since you have been so much from home these last weeks, I've been able to read Sidney. Johnny has read me selections from his 'Discourses Concerning Government.' Johnny's fascinated by it, you know. He was particularly distressed when he learned that the author had been beheaded on Tower Hill back in 1683 for opinions we now think of so highly. Johnny said it seemed so unfair and unjust."

"What a brilliant son we have!" John said. "If the people of America are wise and honest in the choice of their rulers, as we have been in framing the government, they will be happy."

"Yes, it is in the choice of the right men where we must not fail," Abigail interrupted soberly. "For the best of laws can be perverted in evil hands."

"We shall not fail, nor shall my children or my children's children, my dearest Portia." John was stirred. "I feel now that I may die content, knowing that if my children cannot be happy and do well under such a form of government and administration, they will not deserve to be at all!"

Abigail smiled. Her thoughts turned from the budding beauty of her fourteen-year-old daughter to the handsome youth of John Quincy, to charming young Charles and boisterous Tommy. It was good, so good, to be together again. The future stretched out serene and assured. Little did she or John suspect that within two months he, accompanied by his two older sons, would again be crossing the Atlantic Ocean.

But the Adamses were to learn this very soon. John was chosen by Congress to go to France as a plenipotentiary and complete the peace with England.

Abigail was bereft; yet when she insisted that they all go together, John would not hear of it. He spoke of the great cost; moreover he insisted it would be foolish to move the entire family for so short a time as one year.

But the year lengthened into two, three, and four years. During this time young John Quincy accompanied his father's friend, Francis Dana, to Russia. Charles, left alone in a Dutch school, admitted to increasing homesickness. He was finally allowed to return to Braintree with some of his father's friends.

Meanwhile John Adams himself was becoming more and more frustrated. He journeyed from France to Holland, back to France, back again to Holland. In Holland, fatigued and discouraged, he decided to write a series of articles for the Dutch newspapers to inform the Dutch people of his country's fight for freedom, and especially of America's great potential wealth and natural resources. He talked and talked, extolling the United States far and near.

As he made more and more good friends in Holland, John came to think that a Commercial Treaty with the Dutch would make his country less dependent on the French Alliance. He succeeded in putting through such a Treaty and obtained a large loan from the Dutch government.

The year before this, Cornwallis had surrendered at Yorktown and the Revolutionary War had been won.

Now John was ordered to France, where he, Dr. Franklin, and John Jay were appointed to make the peace treaty with Great Britain.

During the first fortnight in Paris, John spent all his time with the British negotiators. When he was finally asked to visit the French foreign minister, Vergennes, he met with an unusually polite reception.

"*Monsieur, vous êtes le Washington de la négociation.*"

It was delightful to be called "the Washington of negotiation." It implied that John would succeed with the Treaty of Paris as General George Washington had succeeded on the battlefield. And so he did.

By January, 1783, the preliminary articles between the three countries were signed, though the Treaty was not finally completed until September of the same year. It recognized the independence of the United States, established boundaries, and gave the United States the Newfoundland fisheries.

Triumphant, John was now ready and eager to return home.

But Abigail had endured her lonely life as long as she could. She was already en route to England, accompanied by Abby!

When John learned of this he sent John Quincy, who had returned from Russia, to meet his mother and sister. The young man remained several weeks in England, but when his mother did not arrive, he returned to his father in France. So the the two Abigails were alone for some time after their arrival in England.

Abigail was now in her fortieth year and John was approaching his fiftieth. Their daughter was a very handsome and self-contained young lady of eighteen. Large, tall, and majestic, as her mother described her, young Abigail had a cool manner which forbade intimacy. Her parents had recently thwarted her first romance, not allowing her to marry the poet and would-be writer, young Royall Tyler. This had not increased her affability.

Later, this same Tyler, who had been a clerk in John's law office, became Chief Justice of Vermont. He also wrote a play, *The Contrast*, produced in New York and Boston in 1790, which was the first American play ever produced by a regular company of comedians. His novel, *The Algerian Captive*, and other novels and plays, satirized American social life.

Abby was excited when John Quincy arrived. She had always adored him. The young man brought letters from his father, but it would be ten days before they could start for Holland, he explained. He smiled meaningfully at his sister.

"What could be better?" John Quincy asked. "Abby and I will have a gay time together!"

It was July, and the gardens at Kew, Ranelagh, and Hampton Court were a joy. The multicolored flowers delighted Abigail. Her daughter remarked quietly on the exquisite miracle of the endless greens.

The round of friends and dinner parties continued. The young people enjoyed themselves immensely. On the eighth of August they hoped to start for Holland.

The evening before, John Quincy took his sister to the theater for a final treat. Abigail stayed at the hotel to finish packing.

Then came an unexpected knock on the door. Abigail hurried to open it.

There stood her husband, his round face smiling, his eyes shining. It had been four and a half years since she had last seen him. She could scarcely believe her eyes. How often she had repeated John Milton's famous lines to herself! She had even written them to John. Now she murmured them, "Sweet, thee is sweet . . . ," as he clasped her in his arms.

While they awaited their children's return, John asked: "Was that actually Milton with which you greeted me?"

"Eve, rather, my dearest friend!" she laughingly replied.

"Ah, yes, I believe I know those lines by heart as well, or better than you!" John, restlessly pacing up and down, began to recite:

" 'With thee conversing, I forget all time,
All seasons and their change, all please alike.
Sweet is the breath of morn, her rising sweet,
With charm of earliest birds . . . ' "

"It was Eve, not Adam, who said that, you know," Abigail interrupted him, just as young Abigail and her brother burst in.

Not only was it wonderful to have husband and father with them, but also delightful indeed that their destination had been changed to France.

For three-fourths of a year the Adams family made

their home in Auteuil, in a country house that John had rented at a bargain. It was not the sort of house that Abigail had been used to; on the contrary. It was a huge place with some fifty little rooms upstairs, not one large enough to make a comfortable bedroom, as her daughter had remarked. The rooms below were enormous, with red-tiled or waxen parquet floors. It was almost without furniture, which was expensive but had to be purchased. The endless servants were a constant annoyance; they cheated and did but little work. It was all most distressing to the thrifty New England housewife.

Yet it was a period of comparative happiness. Abigail made only a few friends, but they were good ones. John kept up his daily walks in the Bois de Boulogne, which the doctor had ordered to restore his health after a dangerous bout of fever. In his leisure moments he sat quietly before the fire reading Plato's "Laws" or taught John Quincy the more difficult Greek and Roman authors, and higher mathematics. He was determined that Johnny should shine at Harvard College, where he planned to send him the next year.

Abigail was often alone. When Johnny had free time he would take Abby into Paris, where they visited the art collections, attended the theaters, and explored the ancient city from one end to the other.

Abigail herself occasionally accompanied them to the theater and the ballet, which had cast its spell over her. She even enjoyed the opera ballet after she recovered from her first shock at the shortness and thinness of the dancers' dresses. But more often she would wander around the garden.

One day in May, Abigail walked under the flowering
chestnut trees in her garden, admiring the various
flowers coming into full bloom. Her thoughts turned
to her younger sons in America. Dear, sensitive
Charles missed her, she knew. How kind he had been
to learn the Scotch song for her and sing it:

> "His very foot has music in't
> As he comes up the stairs."

A better, gentler boy never lived.

> "And shall I see his face again?
> And shall I hear him speak?"

It had been her dearest friend and husband of whom
she was thinking when she first heard the song. Now
her heart went out to the boy of fifteen who was
preparing for Harvard at a school near his uncle's. She
knew Charles missed her more than young Thomas
did. He had scarcely ever had a normal home life with
both parents; he needed normality more than the
others, she felt.

What could be delaying John? Frequently he came
back late for dinner or not before eleven or midnight.
Often Abigail entertained, but more often she was
alone. She could not speak French well and it distressed her to try. Had it not been for her garden she
could scarcely have borne her loneliness.

The twilight was deepening. The first star peeped
out. A faint, perfumed breeze sprang up. Abigail
shivered. Where could John be? Her favorite quotation
from "Paradise Lost" came to her mind. She had

memorized it. In a soft voice she began to recite the words to the empty garden:

" "With thee conversing I forget all time,
All seasons and their change, all please alike.
Sweet is the breath of morn, her rising sweet,
With charm of earliest birds; pleasant the sun,
When first on this delightful land he spreads
His orient beams, on herb, tree, fruit and flower,
Glistering with dew; fragrant the fertile Earth
After soft showers, and sweet the coming on
Of grateful evening mild; then silent night
With this her solemn bird, and this fair moon,
And these the gems of Heaven, her starry train:
But neither breath of morn, when she ascends
With charm of earliest birds, nor rising sun
On this delightful land; nor herb, fruit, flower,
Glistering with dew; nor fragrance after showers;
Nor grateful evening mild; nor silent night
With this her solemn bird, nor walk by moon,
Or glittering starlight, without thee is sweet . . .' "

Abigail sighed; her heart felt as if it would burst. No longer was she separated from her dearest friend for years, but only for hours. Yet how long hours could be, she had learned in Auteuil. She drew her lace shawl closely about her shoulders. Her eyes blurred with tears. She did not see John approaching.

"Why, what are you doing out here? You'll get a chill!" he greeted her, not observing how upset she was.

"In a week we'll be in England and there you'll have no language difficulty, my Portia. Everyone there will speak Portia's, or shall I say, Shakespeare's language?"

John took her arm in his. "I made all arrangements today; that is why I am a little late. Have John and Abby returned yet?"

They moved slowly toward the huge house, which even many fireplaces and dozens of candles could not give the warmth of home.

"I shall miss Mr. Jefferson and a few others, but I shall be happy to go to England," Abigail said, "though methinks there's always a degree of *tristesse* in leaving Paris."

"The Count de Vergennes said to me when I took leave: 'It is a great thing to be the first ambassador from your country to the country you spring from. It is a mark, as the King says.'"

John's greeting from George III, when he learned that John had just come from France, was more disconcerting. "There's an opinion among some persons that you're not attached to the manners of the French," King George III observed.

"That is not wholly a mistaken opinion," John promptly assented. "I have no attachment to any but my own country, Your Majesty!"

"An honest man will never have any other," agreed George III; then he bowed dismissal.

As soon as possible John settled his family in a spacious house in Grosvenor Square, not far from Hyde Park, where John could walk as he had in the Bois de Boulogne.

Then he had a private audience with the Queen,

whom he addressed as he would have any strange lady. Yet she was unable to understand him at all, though she endeavored to be very civil. Two days later came Abigail's turn.

Queen Charlotte held a Thursday Circle. On the previous Thursday, Colonel William Stephens Smith, a handsome young man from New York, former aide to General Washington and now Secretary of the American Legation in London, had been presented. This brilliant colonel, one of the most skillful and gallant officers in the Revolution, was fond of social life and was something of a wit.

It was this Colonel Smith who accompanied Abigail and Abby to the Queen's drawing room. Two hundred or more persons were lined along the walls of a large reception room in St. James Palace, the red brick building which was the London residence of the sovereigns. At two o'clock a bugle announced the arrival of the King and Queen.

Abigail had dressed with care in her best mulberry-colored silk frock, with its low neck filled in with a white muslin yoke. She thought the King a pleasant man. He was some three years younger than John. When the attendant announced Mrs. Adams, Abigail drew off the glove on her right hand, but George III kissed her cheek!

His Majesty then asked if she had taken a walk that day. When she replied in the negative, he seemed surprised and asked: "Why, don't you love walking?"

"I fear, Sire, I am somewhat indolent in that respect," replied Abigail.

Whereupon the King shook his head and passed on! The Queen did no better. Abigail could never forget the ennui of those Thursdays.

But London offered more interesting outlets. She often visited historic Westminster Abbey, with its tombs of sovereigns and poets. In the famous Chapter House the Parliament of the realm had assembled for centuries. Then there was the magnificent Chapel of Henry VII, with its superb fan vaulting, and the sacred shrine of Edward the Confessor. Here in stone was a record of English history, the very fabric of England's life.

In this Abbey, Abigail heard Handel's "Messiah" and knew it to be "the most powerful effect of music I ever experienced . . . when it came to the part of the Hallelujah, the whole audience rose and all the musicians, every person uncovered . . . I could scarcely believe myself on earth. I was one continual shudder from the beginning to the end of the performance." In these words she confided to her daughter that evening.

The theater was marvelous, too. Mrs. Siddons, a very great actress, happily spoke a language Abigail could understand.

Colonel William Stephens Smith, who worked with John and took them to the Queen's Thursdays, soon found young Abby "more than any painter could express or youthful poet fancy when they love." Young Abby's eyes took on a brightness, absent since her early love affair. The stately, self-contained girl was almost gay.

Then came the evening when the Colonel requested permission to accompany them to the play. On their return he formally asked for Abby's hand in marriage. This time John and Abigail consented.

Abby was married in July by the Bishop of Asaph, whom Abigail had found to be "a most liberal man," as she had found the Bishop's family "truly well-bred." Although Abigail, the daughter of a New England parson, did not choose the Church of England for her daughter's wedding, she explained dryly: "The liberality of this enlightened country is such that the dissenting clergy are not permitted to perform marriages!"

John Quincy was now in Harvard. So with their children away, the Ambassador and his lady often sat at home in the evenings and read. One night John decided to visit his old friend Jonathan Sewall, who was living in London. Jonathan had bitterly resented the creation of an American Legation; he had been part of the outspoken group with strong anti-American feelings. But when John saw him again he was deeply moved.

"I don't suppose you even play backgammon?" Jonathan asked, anticipating the negative answer. "Oh, my dear old friend!" Sewall exclaimed. "Why is it men with a tenth of your ability can shine in the Courts of Europe? I can tell you! It is because you refuse to dance or gamble, dress fancily and flirt with the ladies. Worse yet, my dear old David, you are an honest man!"

John nodded, too moved to speak. Jonathan had called him by the old name of "David." It transported him back to Boston, back to times long ago when they were young men together.

"Do you know," Jonathan went on, "you would have made a marvelous Harvard professor. I think you missed your calling when you went from the law to diplomacy."

"I didn't go, Jonathan, my country sent me," John answered quietly.

"Your country! But never again mine! They have robbed me of all I had!"

"No, Jonathan," John disagreed sadly. "It was you who robbed your country, when you left her in her need."

John saw that they could never have anything in common, except the memories of youth. That was not enough, so he quickly took his leave.

Jonathan Sewall soon left London to make his home in Nova Scotia. John never saw him again, but he learned indirectly that one of Jonathan's sons became Chief Justice of Lower Canada; the other son became Solicitor General.

Meanwhile in April, 1787, John's first grandchild was born to Abby. The boy was christened William Steuben Smith.

John had been writing a book which he called *Defence of the American Constitutions of Government*. The first volume was printed in January. It greatly influenced the Federal Constitutional Convention, which met soon after its publication.

In Montagu House Abigail had proudly deciphered on the Magna Charta the signature of her distant ancestor. John could not resist teasing her a little.

"What of your other ancestors back in 1215, Portia? There must have been rather a host of them!" John threw his head back as if in deep thought. "Let me see, how many must there have been? Some three-quarters of a million, more or less, according to my progressive arithmetic!"

Abigail refused to pay any attention to such foolishness; her face was full of satisfaction. She even induced John to go to Winchester where in the days of wicked King John had lived Saer de Quincy. Little did she or John suspect that in the near future the name of their town of Braintree would be changed to that of Quincy!

They traveled about the country quite a bit, going on to Plymouth and Oxford and Blenheim; the country was very fine, but often John would compare it unfavorably with Braintree. Abigail could see plainly that he was as homesick as she. After all, he had been away far longer—almost six years.

Recently he had bought, through his agent, the old colonial home built in the early days of the century by Major Vassall, a wealthy West Indian merchant. More recently it had belonged to Royall Tyler, Abby's first beau. Though not overlarge, this was the most impressive dwelling in Braintree, after Colonel Quincy's own house. During this last year in England John was having a suitable addition built and other changes made.

When the Adamses finally left the Court of St. James and sailed for home, they thought the house would be in a finished state, ready to receive them.

How they planned the details of their home on that return trip! In the dining room, panelled with San Domingo mahogany, they would put the beautiful furniture they had bought in Holland and France. John planned just how he would arrange his books in the new library; he now had thousands of old books, new books, law books, translations of ancient writers, books on government, and all sorts of books. With Thomas Jefferson's it was probably the largest private library of the time. The Lafayette chairs, bought in Auteuil and upholstered in red damask, Abigail decided to put in the east room which was to be painted a soft gray, then called French gray.

Despite these happy plans the voyage seemed overlong, so anxious were John and Abigail to arrive.

As Abigail said: "I have learned to know the world and its value. I have seen high life. I have witnessed the luxury and pomp of state, the power of riches and the influence of titles. Notwithstanding this, I feel that I can return to my little cottage and be happier there; and if we have not wealth, we have what is better— integrity."

FIRST VICE-PRESIDENT OF
THE UNITED STATES

A S THE SHIP ENTERED BOSTON HARBOR JOHN ADAMS was welcomed by a discharge of cannon from the Castle; there was more firing when he appeared on deck. Thousands of people had gathered along the water front. The shouts were tremendous! The Secretary of State for Massachusetts was on hand to greet John. In the gubernatorial coach they drove to the Governor's mansion.

The Governor at this time was his old friend, John Hancock. With his habitual exuberance Hancock insisted that the Adamses return to Braintree (Quincy) in his coach and four, accompanied by light horse. Even the people of his village desired this and planned to come out to meet them. But neither John nor Abigail cared for display; they returned home privately.

When they reached the Vassall place, Abigail simply sat down and wept. The ordered work had not been done; everything was in confusion. Such a swarm of carpenters, masons, and farmers distracted Abigail. Nor was she pleased when John enthusiastically began to stock the farm. She complained of his half-dozen, fine, new cows!

Abigail was feeling her forty-five years. She begged John Quincy, who had graduated from Harvard a Phi Beta Kappa and was studying law, to help them settle. He took five or six weeks off and did wonders. Johnny was very happy to be at home and to see his parents again.

John was content. He had kept the two farms, the one where he was born and the one next door where he and Abigail had lived their early married life. Here, there, everywhere, John roamed, happier than he had been for years, directing and overseeing the work on his own land.

John named the large new house "Peacefields." He had a family seal made for his sons and his sons' sons. It showed a pine tree, a deer, and fish in a sea, all under an arc of thirteen stars. Now that there was peace, John and his children and grandchildren could hunt and fish again freely.

Abby, who had sailed with her husband and child soon after her parents, was in New York; she wrote such plaintive letters that Abigail decided to pay her a visit, for she wanted to see her new grandson, John Adams Smith.

Charles was eighteen and in Harvard; Thomas was a big lad of sixteen. Both gave John much-needed youthful companionship.

How the weeks and months flew! Soon John was chosen the first vice-president of his country; not unanimously, as George Washington was chosen president, due to the political maneuvers of Alexander Hamilton. New York at the same time had been chosen for the first seat of the newly formed Federal Government.

Abigail was delighted. Now she would live constantly near her daughter, who was staying with her husband's family. The Smith girls were charming, Abigail thought, especially grave, young Sally, a tall girl, unaffected and graceful, with a pretty face. Before long Sally was to become the bride of Abigail's favorite son, Charles, thus linking the families a second time.

Charles finished Harvard, where he had been drinking and gambling far too freely. The cheerful, gay youth could not resist temptation. Abigail decided to take him under her wing, so she brought him to New York, where she had taken a pleasant house at Richmond Hill (the present Greenwich Village) with an upper and lower porch in rococo style.

That May they all attended the first Presidential Inaugural Ball, which was held in the large assembly rooms on Broadway (near Wall Street of today). Until after his marriage Charles went to and from his work each day with his father. Thomas was now a student at Harvard and John Quincy was studying law in Portsmouth, where he was in the midst of his first romantic love affair.

While John spent his days in the business of his country, Abigail increased her friendship with General Washington and his wife. She often entertained and attended social functions. The Adamses renewed their friendship, which had started so pleasantly in Paris, with the tall, black-clothed Virginian, Thomas Jefferson. What a splendid talker he was; how well-informed! "Why," Abigail told John, "Mr. Jefferson has a brilliant mind!"

"A French mind," John added. He had found he disagreed in many fundamental principles with Mr. Jefferson.

In 1790 the Federal Government moved to Philadelphia. Abigail was soon very ill. The climate of the Pennsylvania city had never agreed with the Adamses. She suffered from inflammatory rheumatism, and Abby came to nurse her. Perhaps Abby's husband was jealous of his wife's deep affecton for her parents. At any rate, Colonel Smith appeared and "whisked his wife off to Europe," to Abigail's chagrin.

In time for the birth of their daughter, Abby and Colonel Smith returned from Europe. Little Caroline grew into a delightful child, as charming as her uncle Charles had been. Abby's husband promptly purchased a coach and four "like General Washington's." He started to build an immense, elaborate house in New York which he named Mount Vernon.

At first John Adams was impressed by the success of his son-in-law. He even went so far as to say, "I wish my boys had a little more of his activity!" But John did not wish this for long.

Abigail was soon complaining, "I found Abby and her children well; she has grown very fleshy. But she is very lonely up in East Chester where Colonel Smith has moved. It is miles to the nearest neighbor! It is a poor, wild place, but they must retrench! The gambling in land got hold of him. Abby is not to blame in the least."

Such was the sorry end of the coach and four and the great house, all to be "like General Washington's."

Not only Abby's but Charles' situation worried his aging parents. The habit of drinking was proving insidious. He could not resist it.

Of course, there were happy moments in Philadelphia—the richest, gayest city in America. It was actually a cosmopolitan city; all the famous people of Europe visited it.

The ballrooms, filled with gay, exquisitely dressed girls and women and splendidly attired men, could rival those of France. Nor could Europe brag of such beauties as Mrs. Bingham and her sisters, or the Misses Chew and Allen!

John did not enjoy this social whirl as much as his wife did. He preferred the smaller dinner parties, where he and his friends could sit over coffee and beverages and, when they finally joined the ladies, listen to music or witty chatter. He had succumbed to the fashionable manner of dress in France and felt he could hold his own in Philadelphia.

But there were little social difficulties for Abigail to overcome. It was soon apparent to her that due to party animosity no one invited Mr. Jefferson, their close personal friend, and Mr. Hamilton, John's political colleague, to the same dinner party!

More than the social gatherings John enjoyed the life of the city. One day he returned to Bush Hill, the enormous house the Adams had rented two miles from the city, full of enthusiasm over the Butchers' Parade.

"It was an amazing spectacle, my dear Portia," John explained. "I never saw a finer bull. And what do you suppose—he had a wreath of roses and other flowers around his neck, and was accompanied by fiddlers! There were crowds of young people watching it, delighted as I was."

Abigail smiled. "It's pleasant to see you so happy."

"It was extraordinary to see a bull so fancifully adorned," John continued. "It must be some old guild survival, or more likely one from way back in Greece or Rome. It was exciting to find it here, right in the streets of our new world capital!

"The markets, too, fascinate me," John continued. "All the fruits of the earth are collected here and food of every sort as well."

"I know," agreed Abigail. "If we were in town I could go about more. The roads are so muddy and rutty I feel shut up out here."

"We'll go home for the summer, Abigail," John promised. "The yellow fever has commenced. I cannot risk infection."

Once back in Quincy, Abigail remained there tending her own home and gardens.

When John returned to his duty in Philadelphia he became quite bored. The vice-presidency offered him little outlet for his energies. He exhausted all the bookshops. He even tried ice skating, which had become the rage.

The election of 1797 was rather disagreeable. Unfair and nasty attacks were made on John. Bits of his writings were removed from their context and used against him in an effort to prove that he wanted the son of George III as King of the United States! It would have been silly had it not been so dishonest. John knew the venom was not directed against him personally but against the funding policy of Alexander Hamilton, whose object had been to stabilize the currency but which inevitably benefited some people more than others. Nonetheless, John disliked the attacks on himself. Their injustice cut him to the quick.

Abigail had been horrified at the guillotining of Marie Antoinette, Queen of France. She was worried about her two old friends, the Lafayettes, who were in danger as aristocrats. She hoped to receive first-hand information about them now that John Quincy had been appointed Minister to Holland by President Washington. He would be able to get her fashionable clothes in London and Paris, too. She especially wanted a red broadcloth cape trimmed in white fur. These were all the vogue that year.

John Quincy sailed the middle of September, taking his brother, Thomas Boylston, with him as his secretary.

Good, steady Tom had been troubled since childhood with bouts of rheumatic fever. He was repeatedly ill in Europe, but he liked it there and remained to be best man at his brother's marriage at the Church of All Hallows, London, to Louisa Johnson. After the wedding President Washington promoted the young bridegroom from Minister Resident to Minister Plenipotentiary, doubling his salary, and ordering him to Portugal. Later John Quincy was switched from Portugal to Prussia.

A new election was coming up in the United States. As George Washington refused to run for a third term, the contest was between Thomas Jefferson and John Adams.

For eight years John had dutifully filled what he described as "the most insignificant office that ever the mind of man contrived or his imagination conceived." Would he now be allowed to ascend to the position of helmsman of the nation?

Rhymes were being circulated:

> "Daddy vice, Daddy vice
> One may see in a trice
> The drift of your fine publication,
> As sure as a gun
> The thing was done
> To secure you—a pretty station!"

The anti-Federalists, in their bitterness, even tried to prove that John Adams and George Washington had been at odds, which, of course, President Washington promptly and publicly denied. There had never been such mudslinging as in 1797. But when it was over at last, John Adams had seventy-one votes and Thomas Jefferson sixty-eight. This automatically made Thomas Jefferson the vice-president.

The following week John took leave of the Senate with fine memorable words, concluding his speech with the announcement that he could find "consolatory hope [if the legislatures of the States were equally careful in their future selections, which there is no reason to distrust] that no council more permanent than this, as a branch of the legislature, will be necessary to defend the rights, liberties and properties of the people, and to protect the Constitution of the United States, as well as the constitutions and rights of the individual States, against errors of judgment, irregularities, of the passions, or other encroachments of human infirmity, or more reprehensible enterprise, in the Executive, on the one hand, or the more immediate representatives of the people, on the other hand."

John left the city to spend a needed vacation with Abigail on his own farm in Quincy. Among the roses she had brought from Auteuil and which were now blooming in profusion, they would wander hand in hand at twilight, amazed in their hearts at the height to which John Adams, a simple farmer boy, son of a simple New England farmer, had risen.

CHAPTER SEVENTEEN

SECOND PRESIDENT OF THE
UNITED STATES

T HE GREAT DAY CAME. THE SON OF THE BRAINTREE farmer was inducted as the second President of the United States.

John discarded the little sword he had worn when addressing the Senate; he sent back to the stables the four white horses that George Washington had used; he refused to allow the Marshal and officers to *walk* before his carriage.

He wore a suit of light gray. He took care to have no

jewels adorn his suit or shoe buckles. All was plain and simple.

Then John delivered an Inaugural Address of the purest and most genuine republican spirit. First he traced the history of his country during the last twenty-five years. He declared that "the principle of free government, framed upon long and serious reflection, after a diligent and impartial inquiry after truth" was his preference and deserved the love and esteem of all citizens.

He proclaimed that he had never been a party man. He feared, he said, the factions in his own country more than the belligerent powers of Europe. He spoke unequivocally for PEACE, and added that he felt "a personal esteem for the French nation . . . and a sincere desire to preserve the friendship which had been so much for the honor and integrity of the American people."

There was a multitude in the House of Representatives that day, but Abigail was forced to be absent. She had remained in Quincy to nurse John's old mother and her young niece, Mary Cranch. Both died in early April. Soon she was free to join John in Philadelphia. It was pleasantly exciting to find herself the First Lady of her country.

They occupied the same house on Market Street which the Washingtons had used; a larger, finer mansion had been built for the President, but John Adams refused it, as too expensive.

Abigail kept to her old habit of rising at five in the morning in order to have a few leisure hours before eight, when she breakfasted. The latter part of the morning she gave to her family affairs; then she dressed for the day and received guests from noon to two or three o'clock. They dined at home as often as possible and, except on Tuesdays and Thursdays, they dined as early as two o'clock. On those two days they were obliged to entertain. Other days Abigail would drive out for air.

On the Fourth of July they had to keep up Washington's custom of entertaining all the governors, officers, and companies of the city to cake and punch. The thrifty New England housewife was distressed at the expenditure of 500 dollars for this one occasion! By now the President's salary of 14 thousand dollars was worth less than half its real value, due to depreciation of the currency and high prices. It made it very difficult for Abigail to keep the outgo and income balanced.

By the end of July Thomas Jefferson was back at Monticello and the Adamses in Quincy. Once again yellow fever raged in Philadelphia.

John had arranged for the schooling of Abby's older sons; the next year he had Abby and little Caroline come to Philadelphia to live. Something must be found for Colonel Smith, or what would become of Abby?

John Quincy had been sent to Berlin, and Thomas remained with his brother and charming sister-in-law, Louisa.

But Charles continued to worry his father. He had loved this son so well and hoped such great things for him. It tortured John to realize that the talented young man was sinking lower and lower.

The trouble with France preoccupied him and often kept him awake for long hours in the night. Timothy Pickering, the Secretary of State John had retained with the rest of George Washington's Cabinet, was complaining that he was unjustly treated. He demanded "the blessings of honest fame." In justice to the man, John Adams felt that he must reappoint him.

John also appointed his friend, John Marshall, and his old friend, Eldridge Gerry, with whom he had been intimate since his youth. He had complete confidence in Marshall and Gerry. Now that Talleyrand was at the helm in France, John hoped for some satisfactory arrangement.

He poured out his feelings to Abigail one evening when they were alone.

"The state of society has so long been disturbed with wars and revolutions, the sense of moral obligations so weakened, public faith and national honor so impaired, that respect for treaties has diminished almost entirely," John said gloomily.

"I know, my dearest friend, you are beset on every side by self-seeking men."

"What else can one expect when pride, ambition, avarice, and violence have so long gone unchecked?" John looked so sober and troubled that Abigail thought she would try to change the trend of his thoughts.

"Must we have a war with France?" Abigail asked. "Everyone is talking about it and asking."

"Not if I can prevent it!"

John jumped to his feet and began to walk about with his old vigor. "I mean to protect the commerce of my fellow citizens. I may even arm our ships if piracy increases. You see, commerce is essential."

He walked more rapidly, frowning deeply. As Abigail said nothing, he continued:

"If not essential to our existence, at least com-

merce is vitally essential to the comfort, growth, and prosperity of my country. The genius, habits, and character of our citizens is highly commercial; our cities have been formed and exist on commerce. Our agriculture, fisheries, arts, and manufactures are connected with it and depend on it. If it is destroyed by piracy or neglected by the government, it will involve our people in poverty and distress. I must be firm."

"But if you are firm, my dearest friend, will not France declare war and throw us into the arms of the British?"

"No one will declare war on us, nor shall we declare on anyone, if I can prevent it," stoutly declared John Adams, with his old combativeness.

When John received reports from his representatives in France, he was horrified at the perfidy of Talleyrand. He hesitated to give the reports to Congress; when he finally did so, he concealed the names of the greedy French bankers, Talleyrand's puppets, behind the letters x y z. So they came to be known in history as the X Y Z papers.

"Without coast defenses, or a fleet, or even a trained army, America is at the mercy of any foreign power," John had told Abigail.

She had heartily agreed, adding, "The French refugees from the recent revolution, who live here in Philadelphia, cause me uneasiness."

So it came about that John Adams advocated a separate Navy Department when the next session of Congress met. This department was to be distinct from the War Department, and money was appropriated for the purpose and three-year enlistments were approved. All this, however, would take time. Meanwhile John knew his country should walk warily among the predatory nations of Europe.

Alexander Hamilton thought that at last everything was coming his way; by political manipulations he had gotten himself nominated second-in-command of the newly formed army.

He outwitted John Adams there, and again in a more personal matter. John had proposed Colonel William Stephens Smith, Abby's husband, for Adjutant General. General Washington had approved of this office for his former aide, but the nominations had to be confirmed by the Senate. The Senate confirmed every nomination that President John Adams made—with the sole exception of the one of Colonel William Stephens Smith!

Even though it was partly his own fault, Colonel Smith was sorely hurt. In the Revolutionary War he had been a gallant officer.

"Poor fellow," said a friend of John's. "Now he has no prospects at all."

"Poor Abby," thought her father. "My poor, dear daughter. What will become of her and the children?"

To add to his troubles, Abigail had been very ill for the past year and he was alone in Philadelphia.

Luckily, John Quincy was doing very well in Prussia, assisted by his brother, Thomas. Vans Murray, the U.S. Minister to Holland, was cooperating closely with John Quincy. In January, 1799, John's youngest son, Thomas Boylston Adams, returned at last from his long service abroad.

John was delighted to see steady, reliable Thomas, now a well-educated young man in his late twenties, versed in legal and diplomatic laws. John needed his company. They talked over the whole European situation in its relation to the new United States. They talked and talked, this father and son, of the need of peace with both France and England. These talks and the valuable dispatches which Vans Murray had sent by Thomas helped John to clarify his messages to Congress.

As a young man in Boston, when he undertook the defense of Captain Preston, John had done a most courageous thing. He had risked all for what he believed to be right.

Now, as an older man in the seventh decade of life, John Adams again did a most courageous thing. He risked the great reputation he had built up through years of struggle. He was still prepared, as when young, to do what he believed to be right, whatever the cost to himself.

His party would undoubtedly throw him out; even his enemies would not be pleased. But this knowledge did not deter him. He was certain that the country was in no position to stand any war. One section of the country favored France; one England. Any war with either European country would divide this country into violent factions. John Adams had worked all his life for the whole country. He knew he must put his country before his party.

February saw him come to the bravest and most difficult decision of his political career, a decision which earned him forever the sobriquet of "honest John Adams."

Trouble with France had been growing apace. The last American representative had been expelled from the country with scant courtesy. Congress was actively and excitedly discussing the capture of armed French ships by armed American vessels.

Congress was in an ugly mood when John rose and delivered his peace message. Members thought John's calm suggestions smacked of betrayal. His own party was appalled; nor did the Republicans thank him, though they favored France. John's party, who favored England, would have been delighted to have a war with France. Some of them were even ready to go back to the King.

The old New Englander stood alone, against friend and foe, with the sole comfort of his own conscience.

Re-election, of course, had been impossible from the instant John Adams put his duty and the welfare of his country above partisan beliefs. But it was "the most meritorious and disinterested action" of his life, he himself often said.

By the end of September 1800 the treaty negotiations were concluded. His three representatives finally went to France. There they no longer had the corrupt Charles Maurice de Talleyrand-Périgord to deal with, but Napoleon Bonaparte himself! Napoleon proved to be most cooperative.

This so-called "Convention of 1800" affirmed that free ships make free goods. Unfortunately the indemnification of illegally seized goods was overlooked.

But old John Adams was content. As he was to write Thomas Jefferson fifteen years later: "I desire no other inscription over my gravestone than: 'Here lies John Adams, who took upon himself the responsibility of the peace with France in the year 1800.'"

The winter of 1799 to 1800 was the last that the government spent in Philadelphia. Abigail again had her First Lady receptions, where witty talk flowed. In this cosmopolitan city, they could boast a theater. Abigail saw *The School for Scandal* performed by American actors and enjoyed it, though not as much as she had enjoyed seeing "the divine Farren" at Covent Garden, London.

In 1800, forty-five-year-old John Marshall succeeded old Timothy Pickering as Secretary of State. The government moved to the city of Washington.

Abigail wrote her sister, Polly Cranch, a spirited description of what the President and his Lady found when they arrived in Washington:

"I arrived about one o'clock at this place known by the name of 'the city' and the Name is all that you can call so! As I expected to find it a new country, with houses scattered over a space of ten miles, and trees and stumps in plenty, with a castle of a house, so I found it.

"The President's House is in a beautiful situation in front of which is the Potomac with a view of Alexandria. The country round is romantic but a wild wilderness at present.

"But surrounded with forests can you believe that wood is not to be had, because people cannot be found to cut and cart it! . . ."

Their agent did manage to get a few cords, but what were they in such a barn of a house? It was essential that thirteen fires be constantly kept so the family would not freeze. Neither the principal stairs of the President's house nor one room or chamber had been finished.

But Abigail soon made the beautiful Oval Room habitable with their red furniture which had done service in Auteuil. Candles and roaring fires added color and warmth. The foreign ministers in their decorations and the ladies shivering in their ball gowns gave some semblance of a festive air that winter.

The death of their beloved son Charles, at thirty, occurred that December. It saddened John as much as Abigail, though both knew it to be a release from his painful condition. He was living in squalor and misery when his mother last saw him.

Soon Abigail's attacks of rheumatism returned. John became alarmed. By the end of February he packed her off to Quincy where she could be warm and comfortable. Charles' widow, Sally, would be with her. Abigail was fond of Sally and her two daughters.

When the election returns were in, Thomas Jefferson had seventy-three votes, as did Aaron Burr, and John had sixty-five. On the thirty-sixth ballot the House of Representatives chose Thomas Jefferson as president, and Aaron Burr became vice-president. John was not surprised.

Nor was Abigail surprised, but she was deeply concerned as to the future of her country. She had written her sister, Polly Cranch, just prior to her return to Quincy in February:

"What a lesson upon Elective Governments have we in our young republic of twelve years old! What is the difference in character between a Prince of Wales and a Burr? Have we any claim to the protection of Providence, when we have, against warning, admonition and advice, chosen as our chief Magistrate a man who makes no pretense to the belief of an all wise and supreme Governor of the World, according or directing or overruling the events which take place in it? I do not mean that he is an atheist, for I do not think he is—but he believes religion only useful as it may be a political engine, and that the outward forms are only, as I once heard him express himself, mere Mummery. In short, he is not a believer in the Christian system . . . Such are the men we are like to have for our rulers . . . If ever we saw a day of darkness I fear this is one which will be visible until kindled in flames."

These fears were common in the Federalist party when Thomas Jefferson, whom they called "a Jacobin," was elected. Aaron Burr, the vice-president, was too elegant and snobbish to be popular with the simple Braintree couple who had inhabited the White House in Washington so briefly.

The night before Jefferson's inauguration, John Adams worked until nine o'clock, sending in nominations which were ratified without Senate debate, while John Marshall signed and sealed the appointments. This was a precedent set by George Washington. John Adams merely followed in the footsteps of the man who was becoming a sort of god to his country.

CHAPTER EIGHTEEN

"YELLOW LEAVES, OR NONE..."

JOHN ADAMS HAD SPENT A QUARTER OF A CENTURY in the service of his country. He was glad to be home in Quincy. Rarely, if ever, was he to leave "Peacefields" again.

Despite his sacrifices for peace, war came in 1812; not with France, but with England. It was the year before his daughter Abby had come home to die. When she arrived in August she was mortally ill; the operations had proved less satisfactory than the doctors had hoped.

"That is the worst of living to be so old," John told

his weeping wife when Abby died. "You lose your children; it's upside down when it's this way. Only John Quincy and Thomas are left now."

"But we have the darling grandchildren." Abby tried to smile through her tears. "Thomas and his family are near, too. And we have John Quincy's boys with us, even if he and Louisa are far away in Russia."

Soon John Quincy left his position as Minister to Russia to attend the Council of Ghent, where he signed as a plenipotentiary. His wife and youngest son, Charles Francis, whom he had left behind in Russia, had joined him in Paris during the period of Napoleon's return from Elba. They then proceeded to England where, like his father, he was Minister from the United States, from 1815 to 1817.

John Quincy and Louisa wanted their children to join them in England. So the boys left their grandparents. John and Abigail missed them terribly.

But not for long. In August 1817 a carriage drawn by four horses was spied rolling down the hill to the Adams home in Quincy.

"Come, my dear, hasten!" called John Adams, still active in his eighty-third year. Abigail came running to his side. Now seventy-three, she had grown fragile and was often overtired of late.

How proud she was of her oldest son, who had been recalled from his post in England to become Secretary of State in Washington. She knew this was called the steppingstone to the Presidency, and her eyes brightened as she watched him alight from the carriage.

The two older boys descended from the carriage,

and young John, with all the ardor of his grandfather for whom he had been named, threw his arms around Abigail and nearly strangled her. His older brother, George, cried with joy: "Grandmother!" and pushed his brother aside to clasp the old lady in his arms.

Charles Francis, who was to have his tenth birthday very soon, hung shyly in the background. He could not remember his grandparents. He had been only two when his parents took him to Russia.

Old John had sorely missed his grandsons. Now that they were back again, he could count on them to "devour all the strawberries, raspberries, cherries, currants, plums, peaches, pears, and apples," in which the farm abounded.

When their parents went to Washington a month later, George and John were placed in Mr. Gould's Boston Latin School to prepare for Harvard. Only Charles Francis remained in Quincy.

The following fall and winter Charles watched from Abigail's west bedroom window the New England maples turn to various shades of yellow and red. How pretty the trees looked in the autumn, he thought. Grandma would sit in her straightback chair by the fireplace; she was often incapacitated by rheumatism. Grandpa would sit on the other side.

In October 1818 Abigail died of typhoid fever. Had she lived another month she would have been seventy-four. John felt more lonely than he could have believed possible.

Children and grandchildren, even great-grandchildren, were thick as berries on a bush. But of John's contemporaries only Thomas Jefferson remained.

His correspondence with this old Virginian friend was all John Adams had left.

The years passed slowly and quietly. His nieces took tender care of him. Visitors came whenever he felt able to welcome them.

In 1826 Daniel Webster, statesman and orator who had come to see Abigail just before she died, came to visit John Adams. He was familiar with the large country house with its three apartments of equal size below and the gallery leading to the stairway. One was the common room to which strangers were admitted; from the next room, turning suddenly to the right, Webster entered the parlor with its rich but simple furniture. The thick carpets and elegant chairs and sofas with deep cushions made it almost like a European salon; in the next room John had placed the family portraits by Copley, Stuart, and other distinguished painters of his time.

Daniel Webster found John in the parlor, dressed in a green morning gown, his wisps of white hair giving him a childlike appearance. John was serene and untroubled, except for the heat. His nieces were gently fanning him.

When Webster spoke of John Quincy, who was now the Sixth President of the United States, a tear fell from John Adams' blue eyes.

"I'll be ninety-one if I live to October," John announced, adding with labored breath, "a monstrous time for one human being to support."

He motioned with an unsteady hand to his younger niece. She bent and John whispered to her. Then she turned to Mr. Webster:

"My uncle had a letter from an old friend in York, Pennsylvania, this morning. When I read it to him he was so delighted he wants you to hear it, too."

When she handed the letter to Webster, John said, "Read it to me, Dan'l. I'd like to hear your voice."

Softly Daniel Webster read:

"'One of your York acquaintances has recently died. You will recall the man, I think, Peter Dunkel, the son of the widow von Dunkel with whom you often chatted. He became a prominent merchant. She was a baroness, you'll recollect. Peter was a patriot. We were all awaiting his death eagerly, thinking we'd learn the contents of those parchments his mother kept locked up. He'd refused to say what they proved; he scorned men who kept titles when they came to America. Rumor had it he could have been a king, perhaps, or something very great. His descendants were even referred to as royalty. Old Peter would say not one word. After the funeral, the executors came to examine his papers. Imagine their eagerness! The box was empty!'"

Daniel Webster paused in his reading to look at John, who was obviously enjoying himself. He appeared mightily amused, so Daniel went on:

"'Finally the widow, after endless questioning, admitted that she had herself opened the box, but she couldn't read the papers as they were in Latin. Her husband had treasured them so tenderly and secretly, she had come to look upon them as sacred, so she did not want anyone else to touch them. She crept to his coffin in the dark and hid them in it with him. So they were buried with him!'"

"That's what we do with kings here in the United States," John muttered between coughing spasms. "We bury them!"

Daniel Webster looked at the indomitable old man and smiled. That was the New England spirit!

Daniel rose to go and held out his hand. "I hope you feel better now," he said.

"No," retorted John. "I have lived in this old and frail tenement a great many years; it is very dilapidated. And, from all I can hear, my landlord doesn't intend to repair it!"

It was a very warm summer. As day followed day John knew he had nothing more to expect from life. He dreaded nothing so much as the possibility he should "dye on top," like his cousin Sam Adams, who was "a grief and distress to his family, a weeping helpless object of compassion for years."

As July 4th approached, the town of Quincy prepared to celebrate. It was the fiftieth anniversary of the signing of the Declaration of Independence. Some townspeople came to beg John Adams to make an appearance, to say a few last words to the assembled throng.

John refused. He had great difficulty in breathing and had trouble with his tongue when he wanted to speak.

They urged him to send a message at least, but had to be content when John said he'd offer them a toast.

"I will give you," he said, "INDEPENDENCE FOREVER!"

John Adams died on that Fourth of July, when all the bells in every city, town, and village in America were joyfully ringing.

His last understood utterance was, "Thomas Jefferson lives."

But he was mistaken. Thomas Jefferson had died the very same day at his home, Monticello, down in Virginia.

These two friends, who had helped fashion the Declaration of Independence, died on the fiftieth anniversary of the signing of that document. It was a coincidence which was long talked of throughout the world.

> *That time of year thou mayst in me behold*
> *When yellow leaves, or none, or few, do hang*
> *Upon those boughs which shake against the cold,*
> *Bare ruin'd choirs, where late the sweet birds sang . . .*
>   Sonnet LXXIII, by William Shakespeare